£5.99

**Welcome to this fantastic collection of fun and frolics. With stories galore, it's action all the way in this slapstick sensation!**

# CONTENTS

Published in 2001 by Just Publishing Ltd, a wholly owned subsidiary of the Just Group plc. Just Publishing Ltd, Office Block One, Southlink Business Park, Southlink, Oldham OL4 1DE, UK. All rights reserved. No part of this publication may be reproduced, stored in a retrieval system, or transmitted in any form or by any means, electronic, mechanical, photocopying, recording or otherwise, without the prior permission of the publishers. Printed in Belgium. ISBN 1-90-391254-7 TOM AND JERRY and all related characters and elements are trademarks of and © Turner Entertainment Co.
(s01)

5

7

8

9

10

IT'S ABOUT TIME YOU MICE LEARNED THAT CATS RULE! BUT LET ME GIVE YOU SOME ADVICE...

... LEAVE THIS HOUSE AT ONCE!

BOING!

AND SO...

HOW COULD IT HAVE HAPPENED SO QUICKLY?

I MEAN, CATS ARE SO STUPID!

UH-OH! I'VE BEEN SITTING HERE SO LONG I FORGOT ALL ABOUT MY POOR STOMACH!

RUBLUPP

THERE'S THAT APPLE TOM THREW... IF ONLY I COULD REACH IT!

BUT DO I REALLY WANT TO RISK MY LIFE FOR AN APPLE?

11

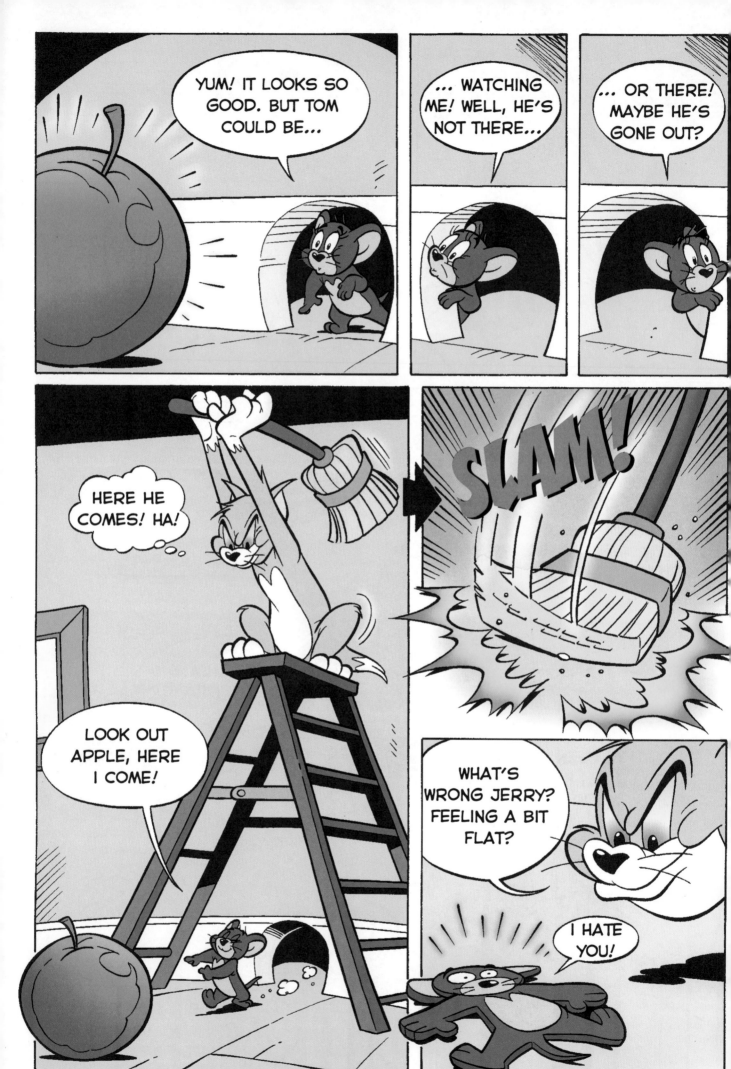

14

LATER...

THERE GOES A PICTURE OF FAILURE... WHAT A LOSER!

DIDN'T I SAY I'D SOON BE RID OF HIM?

HA! HA!

SIGH!

YOU MAY HAVE CHASED YOUR MOUSE AWAY, BUT MINE JUST DISAPPEARED OVERNIGHT!

?!

CONTINUED ON PAGE 23

# Spike and Tyke

**THE END**

WHAT ARE WE GOING TO DO? WITHOUT MICE, WE'RE... GULP... NOTHING!

WE MUST THINK. HOW COULD THIS HAVE HAPPENED?

WELL, IF WE DIDN'T CHASE THEM AWAY... WHO DID?

WHO... OR WHAT? AND WHERE HAVE THEY GONE?

I'VE GOT THE ANSWER. I'VE SEEN IT!

EH?

I WAS JUST CHASING MY MOUSE, WHEN A HUGE ALIEN CAT APPEARED AND TOOK HIM AWAY!

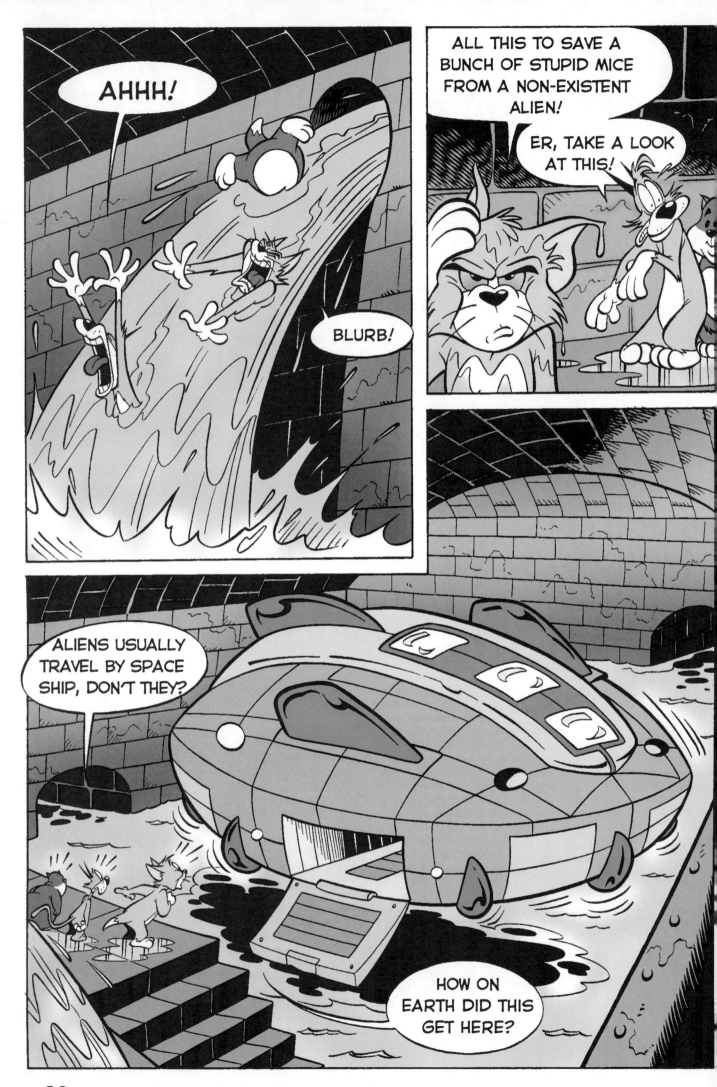

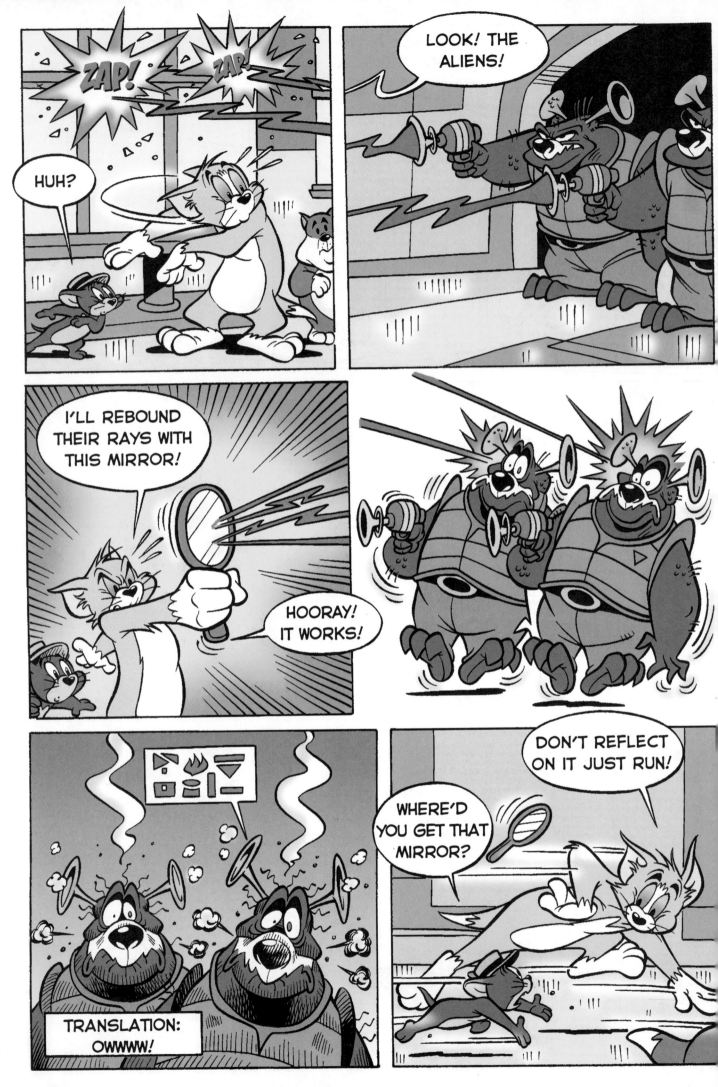

34

REST ASSURED... IF ANY ONE'S GOING TO GET THEIR TEETH INTO YOU, IT'LL BE ME!

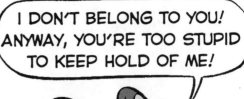

I DON'T BELONG TO YOU! ANYWAY, YOU'RE TOO STUPID TO KEEP HOLD OF ME!

OH YEAH? TAKE THAT!

YOUR LIFE'S IN MY HANDS! YOU SEE, I'M THE BOSS.

ONLY IF I WANT YOU TO BE BOSS!

IT'S CLEAR THAT THIS HOUSE AIN'T BIG ENOUGH FOR US!

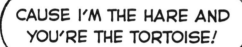

HA-HA! PULL YOURSELF TOGETHER TOM! I'LL GO AND FIND THE SUPERGLUE!

BUT, WHAT'S THE HURRY? I'VE GOT TO KEEP MY STRENGTH UP!

43

GLUF!

THIS DEVICE IS A TRANSLATOR, SO YOU'LL...

... UNDERSTAND ME NOW! YOU HAVE RUINED OUR MISSION, BUT WE WILL NOT RETURN EMPTY-HANDED... WE'LL TAKE YOU TWO WITH US!

UM, WE'LL GET GOING NOW!

COME ON, JERRY! RUN FOR YOUR LIFE!

48

TRANSLATION: GET LOST!

49

THE END

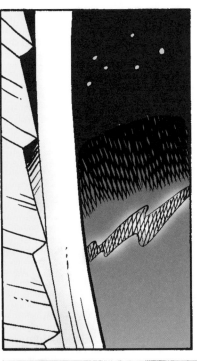

I'M GOING TO PUT A STOP TO THIS RIGHT NOW!

PREPARE TO DIE... INSECT EATERS!

OUFF!

THE END

58

A MORNING, JUST LIKE ANY OTHER MORNING...

... BUT ALL THAT...

# TOM & JERRY
## THE BIRTH OF A HERO!

... IS ABOUT TO CHANGE...

ENTER, AN AMAZING SPACESHIP!

60

65

JERRY, A HERO? HAVE THEY ALL GONE CRAZY? HE'S JUST A MOUSE!

JERRY THE SUPER HERO ALSO SAVED A...

... A BRAVE MOUSE...

COME OUT! I KNOW YOU'RE JUST A ROTTEN RODENT!

PLEASE STAND BACK... I DON'T WANT TO HURT YOU!

YOU, HURT ME? I DON'T THINK SO!

?!

MAKE YOUR OWN ROBOT

FLYIN

SWORDS!

MATHEMATICS

YES! I THINK THAT'S EVERYTHING I NEED!

NOW... WHERE SHALL I START?

HMMM!

AFTER DAYS OF HARD WORK...

I'VE DONE IT!

IT'S FINISHED!

73

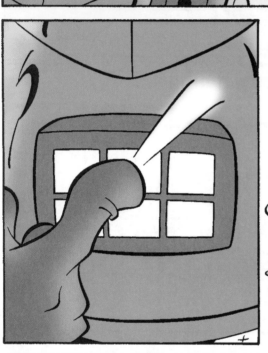

THE END

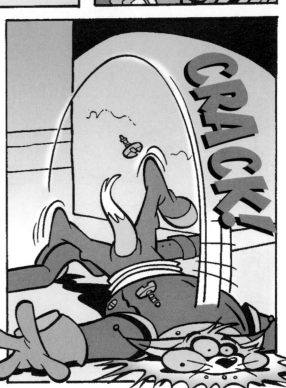

91

# contents

p22

p66  p2  p72  p41

Some material may have been previously published.
Printed and published in Great Britain by D. C. THOMSON & CO., LTD.,185 Fleet Street, London EC4A 2HS
© D. C. THOMSON & CO., LTD., 2004
*While every reasonable care will be taken, neither D. C. Thomson & Co., Ltd., nor its agents accept any
liability for loss or damage to colour transparencies or any other material submitted to this publication.*
ISBN 0 85116 850 7

# Penny's Place

PENNY Jordan's parents owned three cafes, "Penny's Place" and "Penny's" in Chesterford and a brand new cafe in Spain.

Hooray! The holidays at last! Next week, I'll be off to Spain for a whole month!

It must be great having a café in Spain now, Penny. You can visit any time you like.

Yeah, but I have to help out, too. Our manager's on holiday — that's why we're going just now.

Mum's still looking for a last-minute bargain for us. How about *you*, Gemma?

We're going to Barbados for my cousin's wedding!

You're all dead lucky! I'll just be here helpin' Mum!

At least the wages are good, Donna!

Donna's mum was manager of "Penny's Place".

5

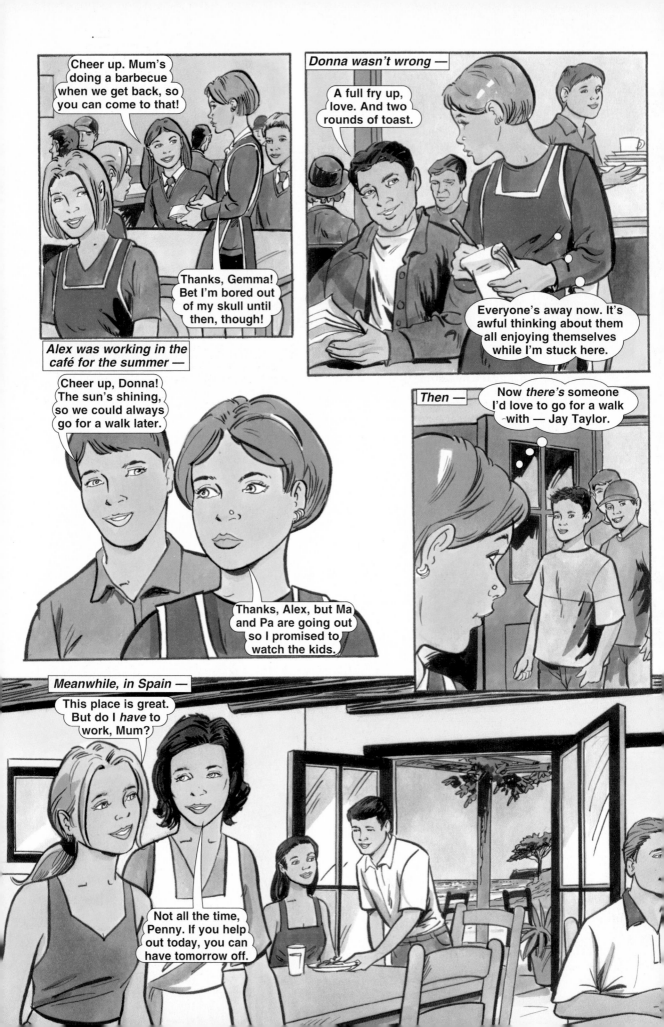

Cool! I could have a swim, read a magazine, lie in the sun . . .

Not until tomorrow. We've got customers.

Poor Donna's stuck at home, while I'm getting paid for working here. Life's tough!

Arlene! Pete! How. . .? What are *you* doing here?

Oh, you know . . . we were just passing.

This is where our last-minute bargain brought us! Cool, eh?

Look who's here, Mum! Do I *really* have to work when my friends are here?

Well, maybe not today. Go and enjoy yourself.

*Back in "Penny's Place", Donna was getting grumpy again —*

Yeah, we're away tomorrow for a few days.

Oh, great! Life just gets better and better — *not!*

Cheer up, Donna! That new film you want to see is on at the pictures.

Yeah, but all my friends are away, doughball!

Well, *we* could go and see it.

I'll have to go with the gang when they come back, Alex, and it would be stupid to go twice.

*And, in sunny Spain —*

I hate being short with Alex — but nothing seems to be going well for me. Penny has all the luck.

It's been fab being able to come and see you. I don't want to go home.

Me, neither. I know I'll be here for another couple of weeks, but it won't be the same without you.

Dad! What's going on? Who sprayed the walls?

Who knows, Penny. It was like this when we arrived this morning.

*There was another cafe nearby —*

We called the police, but they've little hope of catching the culprits, I'm afraid.

Don't worry, Mrs J. We'll soon have things cleaned up.

I wonder . . .

I bet it was those boys. They're probably mad about Mum and Dad opening up a cafe next to theirs.

8

We have no proof, Penny. You can't just run around accusing people.

But, Mum . . .

Leave it, Penny. Your mum's right.

Hi, Donna! How are you doing?

Not so bad now *you're* back, Gemma. Did you have a good time?

Yeah, it was cool! I'll tell you all about it at the barbie — you and Alex are both coming, aren't you?

Try and stop me! This place has been Dullsville with everyone gone.

*Thanks, Gemma!*

Hey, Jay's back, too! Things are looking up at last!

*Things had taken a turn for the better in Spain, too —*

You need help, no?

Same thing happen to our café last year.

What did you say about the vandals earlier, Penny?

Er — I forget, Mum.

I feel awful now!

9

Mmm! He's nice. Maybe I won't be too bored when Arlene goes home, after all.

*Back home, on the day of the barbecue —*

Alex phoned, Donna. He's got a bad headache, so he won't be coming.

Oh! That's a shame but — *wow!* What's *he* doing here?

Oh, Jay? His mum's in some group with Mum. Why?

He's gorgeous, that's why! Come on, we've gotta speak to him.

So —

Jay, this is Donna.

Hi — hey, I know you! You work in Penny's Place, don't you? I go in there quite a lot.

Don't I know it!

*And next day —*

Hi, Alex. How are you feeling?

Much better, Donna. But I was sorry about missing the barbie.

It was great! Jay was there and he . . .

Oh! That would please you.

10

THE END

# HAND-TASTIC!

## HAVE FAB FINGERS AND NAILS WITH OUR MAGIC MANICURE!

## You'll need

an orange stick

a small bowl of warm soapy water

a nail brush

cotton wool

a nail buffer

an emery board

a towel

cuticle remover cream

**1** First, wash your hands and clean under your nails. You can use a nailbrush stroked with soap to do this, or an orange stick tipped with wet cotton wool.

**TIP** Wrap the pointed end of the orange stick in cotton wool to protect your nails from the wood underneath. Dampen the cotton wool with water, and gently clean under your nail tips.

**2** Using the pale side of the emery board, file your nails into a slightly rounded shape. Then remove any rough edges by stroking the emery board up or down the nail edge. This is called bevelling and should stop your nails from splitting.

Rub cuticle massage cream into your cuticles to soften them, then wait for five minutes. The cuticle is the bit of skin at the bottom of your nail where your nail joins on to your finger.

**3**

**TIP** Use the full length of the emery board and don't saw backwards and forwards or you could split your nails. Only use the dark side of an emery board on toe nails.

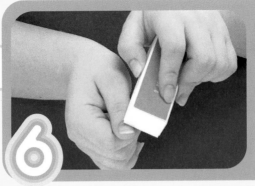

Take the nail buffer, and buff all ten fingernails. This will get the blood running to your nails, and help them to grow stronger. It will also add a lovely shine!

**6**

**TIP**

Run the buffer from the top of the nail to the bottom. Don't buff from side to side - nails are curved, and if you buff from side to side, you'll miss part of the nail!

**7**

Rub a good hand cream into your nails and hands to stop them drying out.

**5** Wash your hands thoroughly using glycerine, fragrance free or moisturising soap - all will be kind to your skin and nails.

Put a fresh layer of cotton wool on the pointed end of the orange stick, and use it to gently push back your cuticles.

**4**

**TIP**

Use fresh cotton wool on your orange stick for each hand. This stops you spreading any bugs.

By now your hands should look clean, healthy and lovely. But for a party or disco, you might want to add your fave nail polish ... or a little bit more! If so, turn over!

# PARTY NAILS!

## You'll need

nail varnish remover

false nails

coloured/sparkly nail varnish

stars

jewels

sequins

### 1

Squeak your nails – this means wiping them with cotton wool soaked in nail varnish remover. This will remove any hand cream and give you a squeaky-clean base on which to work.

### 2

Paint each nail with a thin layer of clear base coat. This will stop any colour from your nail varnish seeping into your nails and staining them. Apply the first stroke down the centre of your nail, and the second and third strokes to the sides. Wait for these to dry.

### 3

Paint each nail with one or two thin layers of your fave nail varnish. Always wait for the first coat to dry before adding the second coat. If you don't it'll be streaky!

### 4

When your nail varnish has dried, paint your nails with a thin layer of clear topcoat. This will help stop your nail varnish from chipping and add a stunning shine.

### TIP

Only use acetone-free nail varnish remover. That way, you won't dry out your nails!

### TIP

Don't leave varnish on your nails for too long, or you will dry them out.

## Extra! Extra! Extra!

For extra special events, go wild with nail stickers, glitter, sequins, stars and all kinds of colours!

Use false nails - then you can be as wacky as you like and remove them next day! Easy!

Nails can be two-tone, studded with 'jewels', dipped in glitter - you name it!

# The TALENT

**K**ay Watson had invited her best friends Marnie, Sarah and Sue around for a chat —

I was thinking about what Miss Smithers said at school today. You know, how everyone has a special talent!

Wow! Miss Smithers must be one talented teacher if she can get *you* to think about anything, Sue!

Very funny, Sarah. Mmmm! That smells nice, Kay.

Thanks! Help yourselves, girls.

Thanks, Kay.

Anyway, we all know your talent, Sue. It's athletics.

Yeah! But what's my best event? After all, I won *everything* at sports day.

Excuse me, I think I feel a yawn coming on!

17

You're clever!

You've got a wicked sense of humour!

And you're pretty.

It's nice of you to say so, but those things aren't really special *talents*, are they?

I guess not!

So Miss Smithers was wrong after all!

*Just then —*

I'm going out for a few minutes, Kay. Mmmm. Something smells good!

It's the chocolate chip cookies I made, Mum. You're just in time to try one.

These are your best yet, Kay. I think I'll take another for later.

*As Kay returned to the table —*

That's it! It's been staring us in the face all the time.

What has?

18

**THE END**

# RED FACED!

Have a giggle at some readers' really, really embarrassing moments! Tee, hee!

My most embarrassing moment was when I tried to cross a small stream on my way home from school. It was only about 50cm wide and I had stepped across it lots of times, but this time I tried to jump, tripped and landed right in the middle. Everyone was watching and they couldn't stop laughing. Mum wasn't so happy about the mess my clothes were in, though.
Chloe, Lancashire

I had just come from swimming and was in a hurry to catch my bus. I wondered why everyone at the bus stop was smiling and giggling at me, but when I got home Mum pointed out that I had put my jumper on the wrong way round. Instead of the V being at the front, it was at the back! Eeerk! I felt really stupid.
Melissa, Dorset

At a disco my friend and I were dancing and saying how horrid we thought another girl's outfit was. We had to talk loudly because of the music, but when the music suddenly stopped, everyone heard us. We weren't half embarrassed!
Shirlie, Bridlington

Last summer my mum and I took my little cousin to her local fete. There was face-painting for the little ones and, although my cousin wanted to have her face done up, she was shy and wanted me to have a go first. Well, I thought it was a bit uncool but, as there was no one I knew around, I had my face painted as a cat. I had just finished when I spotted a boy from my school. I tried to hide, but he had seen me and called out, "Hi, Cat Woman!". My face was painted *and* red after that! Even worse, he told everyone at my school and now all the boys call me Kitty Kate!
Katy, Canterbury

I was in the changing room getting ready for a hockey match. I took out my kit – only to find that I'd brought my brother's football stuff by mistake. I didn't half feel a fool. Luckily my brother didn't have a football game that day, cos he'd have been *really* embarrassed if he'd had to wear my hockey skirt.
Vicky, London

A-A-TISHOO

One school lunch time, while I was eating a bag of crisps, I felt a sneeze coming on. I tried to stifle it, but that only made things worse cos all the crisps flew out of my mouth and I choked and spluttered. I was wiping bits of crisps off my front for hours after. It was *sooo* embarrassing!
Marnie, Doncaster

21

# PETS! PETS! PETS!

**What's your favourite animal? You may not realise it, but your choice of ideal pet says a lot about you.**

### DOG
If anyone is good at sharing, it's a dog fan. You're happy to share anything - no matter what. You're kind and thoughtful and your friendships always last a long time.

### RABBIT
Most of the time you don't worry about things, but if someone or something upsets you badly, it can make a big impression. You're also a hoarder and love collecting things.

### SNAKE
You're the sort of girl who is always organising outings and special events. You're not quite so organised when it comes to tidiness, though, but you're mega generous.

## GUINEA PIG
Guinea pig lovers are sensitive and a little shy at times. You're happiest among friends you know, but when someone asks for your help, you're only too pleased to assist.

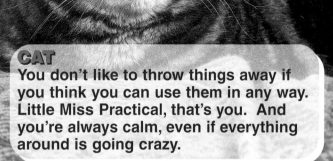

## CAT
You don't like to throw things away if you think you can use them in any way. Little Miss Practical, that's you. And you're always calm, even if everything around is going crazy.

## BIRD
A good desciption of you would be adventurous and carefree. That goes for your dress sense, too! You don't care what other people think, just so long as you're happy.

## HAMSTER or GERBIL
When anyone close to you needs help, you're the one they turn to. You're great at keeping secrets, too, so everyone knows they can trust you. What a star!

## HORSE
You're a no-nonsence sort of girl who doesn't get into a flap easily. Sensible and caring, you work hard at the things you enjoy and your friends mean a lot to you.

## FISH
A calm person, you're great to have around in an emergency. Nothing upsets you and, if others are fussing and panicking, you're a sea of total tranquillity. Cool!

# TAKE OFF!

Take a trip around some top holiday spots with this mega wordsearch. The places listed can read up, down, backwards, forwards or diagonally and letters can be used more than once. Have fun!

| D | J | E | R | S | E | Y | O | L | B | H | I | E | B | O |
|---|---|---|---|---|---|---|---|---|---|---|---|---|---|---|
| U | G | S | I | R | A | P | L | B | G | L | N | C | H | T |
| B | B | Q | P | U | S | A | X | U | A | N | V | I | G | N |
| L | N | L | Q | L | N | E | O | F | J | N | E | N | M | E |
| I | N | R | A | D | Y | R | D | R | D | P | R | I | Y | R |
| N | O | O | U | C | O | M | R | O | D | I | N | E | B | R |
| T | O | D | T | B | K | L | O | C | H | O | E | M | E | O |
| A | N | R | R | H | O | P | O | U | R | R | S | A | T | S |
| O | Z | A | A | N | G | R | O | C | T | X | S | J | A | A |
| J | C | I | D | F | K | I | A | O | V | H | U | O | G | T |
| S | U | O | B | A | D | I | R | O | L | F | R | R | R | H |
| Z | N | E | C | I | N | E | V | B | L | R | P | C | A | E |
| B | O | R | D | E | A | U | X | K | R | O | Y | A | M | N |
| B | A | R | C | E | L | O | N | A | D | N | C | R | X | S |
| S | W | A | N | S | E | A | M | A | L | A | G | A | C | Y |

**20**

**05**

| | | | |
|---|---|---|---|
| ATHENS | CYPRUS | LONDON | PLYMOUTH |
| BARCELONA | DUBLIN | MAJORCA | RHODES |
| BENIDORM | FARO | MALAGA | SCARBOROUGH |
| BLACKPOOL | FLORIDA | MARGATE | SORRENTO |
| BORDEAUX | IBIZA | MINORCA | SWANSEA |
| BRIGHTON | INVERNESS | NICE | TORQUAY |
| CORFU | JERSEY | OBAN | VENICE |
| CORK | LLANDUDNO | PARIS | YORK |

26

Ta, Miss Angel! Now I'll be able to earn some pennies to support myself.

*"Sure enough –"*

Give the busker some coins, darling. She plays such sweet tunes.

Here, girl.

Ta, mister!

*"I earned enough to rent a room –"*

I've done well for meself. If Miss Angel were here, she'd be proud of me.

It's a tiny room but it's — oh! What was that noise?

*"I looked across the landing –"*

A huge family — all crammed in a room the same size as mine! Poor things!

*"So, whenever I could, I handed in some money –"*

Here, Mrs Martin. That should buy the nippers a meal.

Bless you, Annie. You're a good girl.

*"Soon, it was Christmas –"*

Are you going busking, Annie?

Not compared to Miss Angel, I'm not. She worked herself to death for us.

Yes. I should get some good takings. Folks is generous at Christmas.

I'll buy you all a big pudding to share!

Will you, Annie?

Ooh! Ta!

You shouldn't, Annie. You're so good to us, and we can't pay you back.

That don't matter. I enjoy treating the kiddies.

*"I played for hours, and –"*

There's enough for a pudding and more. We'll have a feast.

*"But –"*

No!

Give us the 'at, darlin'!

Come back, thieves!

All my money gone! Folks is going home, now. I'll never earn enough to buy a pudding at this late hour.

THE END

30

# TREE-MENDO

Transform an old Christmas tree into the coolest — and nicest smelling — around this year. Our original orange 'baubles' are cheap and easy to make and look great with plain or coloured lights. So why not give them a go this Christmas?

## WHAT YOU NEED

A few small oranges or mandarins
Pretty narrow ribbon
Some whole cloves
Powdered cinnamon

Ask an adult to help you cut the oranges into thin slices with a sharp knife. Then place them on a baking tray and pop in a cool oven for several hours, until they are dry and beginning to turn golden.

When the oranges are completely dry, cut lengths of ribbon and use it to tie two orange slices together. You will probably find that spaces for threading have appeared in the dried orange flesh but, if not, use a large blunt darning needle to help you thread the slices together.

Before hanging on the tree, stud the decorations with a few cloves, or sprinkle with a little powdered cinnamon.

## TIP

The cinnamon smell will last even longer if you sprinkle a little of the spice over the oranges before you put them in the oven. Don't overdo the spice at this stage, though, or the colour of the fruit will be spoiled.

US!

Tie the ribbon in a pretty bow, then a knot. Remember to leave tails of ribbon as they will be used to tie the decorations to the tree.

If properly dried, these 'baubles' will last ages - and go on smelling Christmassy right over the festive season.

Add extra sparkle by spraying some of the fruit with glitter spray.

Always ask an adult's permission before using kitchen equipment.

# Funky Puzzles!

## ANIMAL MAGIC!

Quickly – change just one letter to turn these animals into different creatures with this easy-peasy puzzle.

Make MONKEY a member of the horse family.
Turn DOE into a barking animal.
Make CAT a mammal that flies.
Change MOUSE into a large American deer.
Alter PUG to create a small insect.

## OOPS!

Which three pop princesses are looking less than lovely?

## FAB FOUR!

Rearrange these letters four times to make four different words:
EMAT

## SOMETHING FISHY!

| | | | | | | |
|---|---|---|---|---|---|---|
| **1** | | | | F | I | S | H |
| **2** | F | I | S | H | | | |
| **3** | | | | F | I | S | H |
| **4** | F | I | S | H | | | |

Fill in four words of four letters to complete these fishy words, following the clues below.

1. A special shaped sea creature.
2. Something savoury to eat.
3. Cool-coloured swimmer.
4. A round glass container.

# BEST BOY!

Which of the following Busted boys' names appears most in this wordsearch, reading up, down, backwards, forwards or diagonally: CHARLIE, JAMES or MATTIE?

```
A M J A M E S C
J M A T T I E H
J A M E S L T A
A T E C E R T R
M T S H M A I L
E I L R A H C E
S E M T J C A S
E I T T A M E C
```

# IN THE BOX!

Can you find these top TV programmes hidden up, down, backwards, forwards or diagonally in our box.

BLUE PETER, CD UK, DAWSON'S CREEK, EASTENDERS, FRIENDS, HOME AND AWAY, ROBOT WARS, THE CHART, THE SIMPSONS, TOP OF THE POPS.

```
D H O T H T C A E T W T
A O N M E D H R E H H O
W M B L U E P E T E R P
S E C K U P O N C S A O
O A E S A L O H V I E F
N N L Y W E A E B M O T
S D N E I R F Y C P A H
C A L L T E D L O S U E
R W S R A W T O B O R P
E A I S B R I L O N E O
E Y O M I H W N E S V P
K S E A S T E N D E R S
```

## ANSWERS

**BEST BOY!**
James appears most in the wordsearch.

**SOMETHING FISHY!**
1. Starfish,
2. Fishcake,
3. Goldfish,
4. Fishbowl.

**FAB FOUR!**
TAME, TEAM,
MATE, MEAT.

**OOPS!**
1. Kelly Osbourne,
2. Kylie Minogue,
3. Beyonce

**ANIMAL MAGIC!**
MONKEY = DONKEY,
DOE = DOG, CAT = BAT,
MOUSE = MOOSE,
PUG = BUG.

'M doing an article on Moorside's ghosts for the school newspaper," Rachel announced, tucking into chips and beans.

"You mean the White Lady who haunts the playing fields? *Everyone* knows about her," Jane snapped. "I'd rather talk about the Christmas disco. You still haven't got a partner, Josie."

Josie shrugged. "So? I don't fancy any of our lot."

"There are at least two other spooks at this school," Rachel interrupted, waving her fork.

"Like, who?" Jane frowned.

"Read it in the paper!" Rachel replied, and stuffed her mouth with more chips.

★ ★ ★

Josie stood at the back of the hall watching her friends. She'd had a great night and, despite not having a regular partner, had danced almost every dance. Now the slow dances were due to begin. Josie frowned. She didn't want to be asked for a slow dance. She might be pestered for a date and she didn't want to date *anyone*.

Then she noticed the flight of stairs leading on to the balcony. She decided to head up there and enjoy the rest of the party alone. She slipped quietly out of the hall and, moments later, settled on a bench overlooking the disco.

As she expected, the music slowed. Some of her friends sloped off to tables scattered around the hall, whilst others moved closer to lads they fancied.

Smiling, Josie watched them through the rails.

Suddenly, someone behind her spoke.

★ ★ ★

"Fed up with the party?"

Josie spun around to see a boy about her age standing in the shadows. At first she thought one of her mates had followed her. Then, as he moved into the disco lights,

# Let's Dance!

she realised she didn't know him. He had dark hair which curled on to his collar. And his face was pale and likeable, with almond shaped eyes.

"Fed up?" she repeated. "Not really. I just thought it would be cool to watch the slow dances from the balcony."

"Me, too," the boy replied, moving beside her. "I like to watch all the dances from up here."

"Have you been here all night?" Josie asked, surprised. "Didn't you fancy coming down for a dance?"

The boy grinned easily and she warmed to him.

"I've not danced for ages."

"Why?" Josie smiled, enchanted with this stranger.

"Shy, I guess," he replied.

The two of them gazed over the balcony in silence. Josie realised with shock that she suddenly wanted to dance with this stranger whose name she didn't even know.

As if reading her mind, the boy reached out and gently touched her arm.

"Would you dance with me?"

Josie stepped towards him and pressed her cheek against his. They danced and danced, slowly gliding round the balcony in shadowy darkness.

Then a clattering from the stairs jerked Josie back to reality. She and the boy flew apart as Rachel and Jane burst into view.

"What are you doing up here?" Jane demanded.

"I — I'm dancing," Josie replied, cheeks flushing stupidly.

"On your *own?*" Jane exclaimed.

"No . . . with . . ." Josie turned to the boy, realising she still didn't know his name.

But he was gone. She scanned the dark balcony to find him.

"I don't understand," she stuttered. "He was here a minute ago! You must have seen him!"

"No," Jane replied, staring at her strangely. "We just saw *you* — swaying about on your own."

"But I was with him for *ages!*" Josie replied indignantly.

"What did he look like?" Rachel asked, eyes wide with excitement.

"He was about our age and very cute. Not one of our lot."

"Oh, Josie," Rachel gasped. "I think you've been dancing with the boy on the balcony!"

"Boy on the balcony?" Josie repeated, vacantly.

"One of the school ghosts!"

"Rubbish!" Jane retorted, marching back off downstairs. But Rachel didn't follow her. Instead, she stared at Josie enviously.

"He's been seen up here several times over the past twenty years. But no one has ever talked to him before, much less *danced* with him!"

She grasped Josie's arm. "I must interview you for the paper — right now!"

"In a minute," Josie replied, a strange, empty feeling swallowing her up.

Rachel nodded, as if she understood, then retreated down the stairs.

Josie turned and gazed into the darkness of the balcony. She stood there for several minutes, watching, hoping, and somehow dreadfully disappointed.

Then, an idea occurred to her, and she smiled.

"Till the next dance," she whispered to the nothingness.

Then she walked towards the stairs.

The End

# It's MAGIC!

Ever watched a magician and wondered how they did their tricks? Read on for some amazing magic tricks – plus the views of Tamara who tried them!

## TRICK ONE

Amaze your friends by making a gold wand turn black!

### Preparing the trick

1. Make your 'wand' by sticking white paper to both ends of your pencil.
2. Cut the gold paper to the same length as the black part of your wand.
3. Wrap the gold paper around your pencil and glue it to make a roll.

### Tamara's tips

"It was quite fiddly getting the gold paper to be just the right length to cover the black part of the wand. Then, when I was practising the trick, the newspaper kept getting stuck on the wand! But, when I eventually did get the trick to work, everyone was very impressed!"

### You'll need...

Gold paper
A black pencil
Glue
A newspaper

### The performance

Hold up the gold wand then, after letting everyone see the newspaper unfolded, roll it around the wand, leaving one end sticking out. (Make sure all the gold is covered though.) Chant the magic spell –
Eeny, meeny, miny, mack, watch my gold wand turn to black!
Hold out the wand and grasp the newspaper roll with one hand, while pulling the wand free with the other. As you do so, the wand will come out black and the gold paper will remain inside the newspaper. Scrunch up the paper and put it in the bin to dispose of the evidence.

# TRICK TWO

Make a thimble change colour — wow!

## You'll need...
A thimble
Another thimble, larger
and different in colour
A handkerchief

## Preparing the trick
Make sure the smaller thimble fits exactly inside
the other larger one.

## The performance
Hold up the thimble on your finger. Unknown to your
audience the other smaller thimble is underneath it.
Cover the thimble with the handkerchief.
Say the magic spell — *Imble, gimble, let's be nimble!*
*Change the colour of my thimble!*
Pull off the handkerchief, lifting off the larger thimble
at the same time. Keep the larger thimble hidden in the
handkerchief.

## Tamara's tips
"I found it quite difficult to get thimbles that were
different sizes. The worst bit was at the end, trying to
keep the other thimble hidden. I'd advise you to wear
trousers with large pockets to stuff the handkerchief
and thimble into afterwards. It was great fun, though!
Everyone cheered."

# Girl's outfit from Rubie's Masquerade.
For stockists, telephone 0871 871 9990

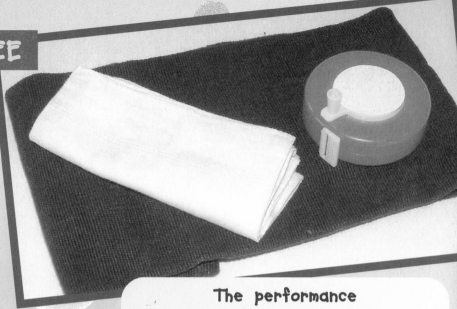

## TRICK THREE

Frighten your friends with a 'ghost' that appears in your handkerchief and 'floats' in the air.

### You'll need...

A large handkerchief
A small cylindrical tape measure
(the rigid type that locks)

### The performance

Put the tape measure and handkerchief in your pocket. Reach into your pocket and take out the handkerchief. As you do so, pull out the tape measure – hiding it in the palm of your hand so no one can see it. Keeping the tape measure hidden, use the thumb and forefinger of each hand to hold the handkerchief at the top corners so people can see there is nothing hidden inside.

Say the magic spell – Hold your breath and gather near. Phantom, Phantom, please appear!

Drape the handkerchief over the hand holding the tape measure. Lift it off and, as you do so, pull up the end of the tape measure under the handkerchief so it sticks up. It will look as if there is a ghost there.

### Tamara's tips

"I needed a lot of practice to hide the tape measure properly in the palm of my hand and my hands felt really stiff afterwards. But it was a great success. I was almost convinced there was a ghost there."

42

44

45

46

I've had a reply from Mavis Scott. She says she hardly ever checks the site and was thrilled to see my name. She wants to meet up.

But I thought she was too boring to contact!

Mmmm! But maybe she's changed as much as Helen has.

Why don't you take a chance? I'll come with you, in case it's a disaster.

*So, a couple of days later —*

I don't know about Mum, but I'm nervous. Mavis is bringing her daughter, too — hope she's not a swot!

There they are. Look she's got a copy of the magazine — just as we arranged.

But she looks like . . .

Mavis? But you're Ruth Jackson from next door.

I don't believe this!

Jackson is my married name — and I started using my middle name soon after I left school. I always hated being called Mavis.

But you look so different and you've got a daughter! I've never seen her around the house.

47

# MANDY'S Mega

**A** Animals! We just can't resist cutesy little animals, can we? Perfect pets or posy posters – we just adore them all. And there are lots to look at in this book. A is also for apples, ankles, advertisements and aardvarks – which certainly aren't adorable!

Little boys Blue – the best band!

Chocolate, chocolate, chocolate! And cheesecake, too! Cooooo!

**C** Chocolate! Mmmmm! What can we say except "give us more!!!!". C also stands for cheesecake, crisps, chips, cookies and cream. Coo!

**D** Diary! A diary can be fun or serious – or even a bit boring, if we're truthful. But one thing it always is, is secret. Anyone who looks at someone else's diary is not to be trusted! Other Ds we kinda like include dads.

Diaries are top secret, so DO NOT PEEK!

**B** Boys! Love 'em or hate 'em, we certainly can't ignore them – well, not all the time! And we never want to ignore the boys from Blue or Busted, do we?

**E** Exercise! We know it's good for us, but we can't always be bothered. But do try to make time for a little each week. Remember, swimming or skating can be fun! E is also for excuses – especially the ones we use when we don't want to exercise.

# A to Z

**F** Football! This used to be for the lads only, but now girls can be just as involved as boys – and that's playing, not just watching. F is also for friends (pals) and Friends (TV prog).

Friends! Gone, but not forgotten.

**G** Girls! It's as simple as that. We are the best, after all. Also gorgeous, great, good........

If you wanna get ahead, get a hat! They're hot!

**K** Karaoke! We may not like to admit it, but we love this cos we can kick up a storm trying out all our latest dance moves while singing along to Kylie.

**J** Justin Timberlake! Need we say more?

Justin – just perfect, with or without his hat!

**H** Hats! Hats are cool – and that's official! Whether it's sun hats for summer or cosy hats for winter, we love 'em!

**I** Ice cream! Especially if it's covered in chocolate, or has a flake stuck in the top.

**L** Lottery! We may be too young to play, but it doesn't stop us dreaming about what we'd do if we struck lucky and won lotsa lovely lolly!

**M** Mobile phone! How did we manage to exist without our mobiles? Mind you, it would be hard to exist without money, mirrors, mums and the Mandy Annual, either. Mmmm!

more on page 68.

# Hi, There!

e-mails, phonecalls or letters? What's the best for you?
Try our fun flowchart and find out.

## START

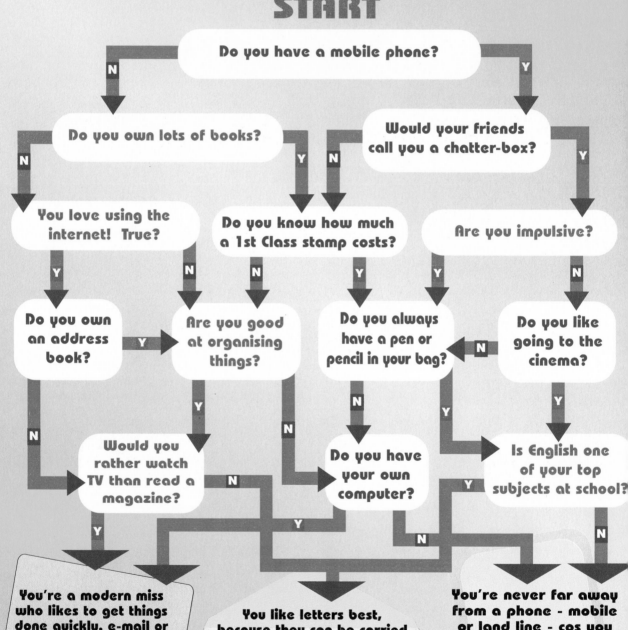

Do you have a mobile phone?

N — Do you own lots of books?

Y — Would your friends call you a chatter-box?

N — You love using the internet! True?

Y — Do you know how much a 1st Class stamp costs?

N — Are you impulsive?

Y — Do you own an address book?

Are you good at organising things?

Do you always have a pen or pencil in your bag?

Do you like going to the cinema?

Would you rather watch TV than read a magazine?

Do you have your own computer?

Is English one of your top subjects at school?

You're a modern miss who likes to get things done quickly. e-mail or texting is ideal for you because it means you can contact your many mates all at once - leaving more time for fun!

You like letters best, because they can be carried about and read over and over again whenever you want. You also find it quite exciting when the postman brings a special letter - just for you!

You're never far away from a phone - mobile or land line - cos you just *love* to chat! You like the fact that phoning is instant and you can spend hours (and pounds!) catching up with gossip.

# A Friend For Keeps!

57

The End

# starscope

## What do the stars hold in store for you in 2005? Read on to find out!

### ARIES    March 22 - April 20

Aries girls are well organised and like to take the lead. These traits should come in very useful in the second part of the year, when you may find yourself having to organise more than you expected. Your ruling planet is Mars, and this means you are energetic and brave - but it also means you have to work hard at times to control your temper. A friend could start to act strangely. Try to find out what is bothering her and help out in any way you can. She'll appreciate it.

*Lucky month:*     **August**
*Lucky colour:*    **Lime green**
*Lucky number:*    **5**
*Lucky word:*      **Dream**

### TAURUS    April 21 - May 21

When it comes to handling money, you're the best. This means that you're always in demand when your mates are looking for help with shopping or bargain hunting. You're also mega popular - with loadsa friends and very few enemies. But be warned, your ruling planet, Venus, can make you a little lazy at times and you sometimes find it hard to make decisions. You may be called on to take the lead in some project this year. Don't be afraid to say what you really think.

*Lucky month:*     **January**
*Lucky colour:*    **Orange**
*Lucky number:*    **9**
*Lucky charm:*     **Shell**

### GEMINI    May 22 - June 21

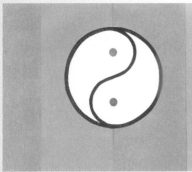

If there's a party around, then you'll be at it. In fact, you'll probably be the organiser, cos there's nothing you like better than parties or outings with lots of friends. Your ruling planet is Mercury and this means that you are likely to be interested in lots of different things - including school. But be warned! Trying to do too many things at the same time is not a good idea. A new hobby may lead to friendship and lots of fun. This could be a drama or music group of some kind.

*Lucky month:*     **September**
*Lucky colour:*    **Brown**
*Lucky number:*    **12**
*Lucky letter:*    **R**

### CANCER    June 22 - July 23

When a friend has a problem, the person she's most likely to turn to is you. You're kind and helpful - and a very good listener. Your main fault is a tendency to be dreamy and forgetful at times, but your gentleness means you're never short of friends. As you are ruled by the moon, you are likely to be quite clever and choose to wear silver jewellery rather than gold. A letter, phone call or e-mail from someone you had almost forgotten could have you changing your plans this spring.

*Lucky month:*     **March**
*Lucky colour:*    **Grey**
*Lucky number:*    **8**
*Lucky flower:*    **Rose**

MORE ON PAGE 72

59

# BIG SISTER!

If you've ever watched Big Brother on TV you'll have seen how hard it is to live in a house with the same people around you all the time and with the cameras watching your every move. How do you think you'd fare if you had someone watching you all the time? Answer **TRUE** or **FALSE** to the following questions to find out if living in the Big Sister House would make you smile - or frown!

**1.** You love meeting new people.

**2.** You don't mind doing your fair share of household chores.

**3.** You always like to win at any kind of game.

**4.** If you didn't have a TV to watch, you'd be totally bored.

**5.** You can keep yourself amused for hours on end.

**6.** You enjoy new challenges.

**7.** You're not too good at speaking to people you've just met.

**8.** You think of yourself as shy.

**9.** If things don't go your way, you're likely to burst into tears.

**10.** You love doing things for a laugh.

## Now add up your score.

| | | | |
|---|---|---|---|
| 1. | True 2 | False 1 |
| 2. | True 2 | False 1 |
| 3. | True 2 | False 1 |
| 4. | True 1 | False 2 |
| 5. | True 2 | False 1 |
| 6. | True 2 | False 1 |
| 7. | True 1 | False 2 |
| 8. | True 1 | False 2 |
| 9. | True 1 | False 2 |
| 10. | True 2 | False 1 |

**11 - 12**
You'd never cope with being in the Big Sister House — but as you wouldn't want to try, anyway, it doesn't really matter, does it?

**13 - 15**
You like a bit of adventure from time to time, but the Big Sister House isn't really your idea of fun. You prefer to be your own boss.

**16 - 20**
Wow! You'd be a natural for the excitement and challenge of living in the Big Sister House. You'd love it!

# mmmm! flapjacks!

## Here's a simple recipe for one of our favourite tasty treats.

**You will need:**

**250g rolled oats**
**125g butter**
**75g golden syrup**
**a little grated orange zest**
**cooking oil**
**a baking tray** (approx 19cm x 27cm)

**What to do:**

1. Switch on the oven to 180°c/gas mark 4.
2. Grease the tray with a little oil, making sure to get some oil right into the corners.
3. Place the butter, sugar, syrup and orange zest in a pan. Heat gently, stirring to stop the mixture from sticking, until the sugar dissolves.
4. Remove the pan from the heat and add the oats.
5. Mix thoroughly before pouring the mixture into the baking tray.
6. Using a pallete knife, spread the mixture evenly over the tray.
7. Place in the centre of the oven for approx 20 minutes - or until the flapjacks are golden.
8. Carefully remove the tray from the oven and let the flapjacks rest for ten minutes.
9. Cut into even-sized pieces.
10. Invite some friends round and enjoy!

**Tip** For something really special, try pouring some melted chocolate over the flapjacks before cutting into pieces. **Mmmm**

**\*Always ask an adult's permission before using kitchen equipment.**

# Mirror,

Almost every girl owns at least one mirror - but did you know that there is a lot more to mirrors than just being simple looking-glasses? Read on to discover some interesting - and some scary - mirror facts.

There are lots of superstitions and beliefs associated with mirrors, most of which started in the dim and distant past, when it was believed that a mirror actually reflected the soul of the person looking into it. As vampires (and some witches) were believed to have no souls, they could be identified by making them look into a mirror. Ooooh! Spooky!

One mirror superstition which has been around for ages is the belief that breaking a mirror will bring seven years bad luck. This probably stemmed from the times when a mirror was an expensive item. Breaking it would, therefore, be considered a great loss – especially in the case of a servant who broke a mirror belonging to her employer. The cost of replacement would probably be taken from the girl's wages. If you are unlucky enough to smash a mirror, however don't despair cos you can lessen the 'curse' b carefully wrapping the broken pieces in fabric (preferably red) and burying them in the ground. According to legend, this reduces the seven years to seven days. Mmmm! Personal we think you should ignore all this silly talk and throw the pieces safely in the bin.

Other mirror superstitions say that a bride should neve look at herself in a mirror once she is fully dressed, as t do so will bring bad luck. Before taking a final look at herself, she should lay down her bouquet or remove a glove or something. If she does look, however, the bad luck can be cancelled by adding something simple, like a hair pin or a piece of jewellery.

# Mirror!

Another old wives' tale states that it is unlucky for a girl to look at her reflection for too long, especially after midnight. This was probably invented to stop young girls from becoming too vain. Likewise, telling girls that they would never marry if they looked at themselves in a mirror by candlelight, would *definitely* discourage vanity.

There are some romantic superstitions associated with mirrors, too. It is said that a girl can tell how many years it will be until she marries by standing on a stone with her back to the full moon and a mirror in her hand. If she holds up the mirror she should see the reflection of the moon surrounded by lots of 'mini-moons'. Each mini-moon counts as a year until she marries – although it sounds more like a damaged mirror to us! Also, if you really fancy a boy you should be careful not to look into a mirror at the same time as him, cos that means you'll never go out together. Well, *some* people believe it!

**Whether or not you believe all these old mirror stories, there can be no denying that mirrors are very useful. Not only do they show us how we look, but they can also be used as decorations. A large mirror hung on a wall can make a small room look bigger or, if a light is placed in front of a mirror, it can make a dark room seem brighter.**

Mirrors come in all shapes and sizes and it can be interesting to look around junk shops and jumble sales for old mirrors. Broken or damaged frames can be repainted, or decorated with beads or shells. It's fun to do – and the end result will be original and cool! Just be careful not to break the glass, because you never know........

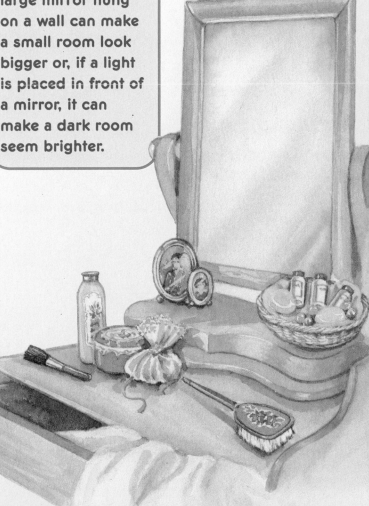

# In The Spot

We've all heard of showbiz dynasties, where several members of the same family become actors, but did you know that families of *dogs* can be stars, too? We took Alice and Joanna Norman along to meet one of the busiest canine dynasties we know.

The girls meet Spencer and his son, Porter.

Dog trainer Carole Lumkin has been training Great Danes for twenty years. Her dogs have appeared with many famous people and, as well as taking part in TV shows such as Blue Peter, also appear in adverts and on CD covers. One even 'starred' as Mr Darcy's dog in the TV adaptation of Pride and Prejudice. Wow!

Say "hello", Grandpa Hogan.

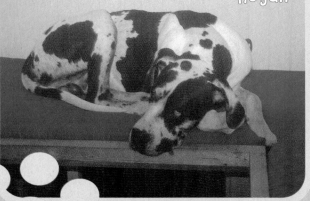

Hogan

Porter

# ight

TJ

All Carole's dogs are trained to do little 'tricks'.

Paws off the table, please!

Shut that door...

...and that drawer!

At the time we visited, Carole had four adult males and a new, four-week old puppy called Porter. While the dogs are very big, they are also very well behaved and friendly — even towards TJ, the cat who shares their home.

Spencer

Wilson

Chandler

Many thanks to Carole Lumkin for her assistance with this feature.

You're not really into fashion. True? **Y** **N**

Are you chatty? **Y** **N**

Would friends say you're cool? **Y**

You laugh a lot. True? **N** **Y**

Do you feel nervous when meeting new people? **N** **Y**

**START**

Would you ask a boy you fancied to dance? **N** **Y**

Do you blush easily? **N** **Y**

Is your fave colour black? **N** **Y**

Is your homework always done on time? **N** **Y**

You always swot for exams - true? **Y** **N**

**N**

On Hallowe'en would you rather go to a party than a cemetery? **N** **Y**

Is wearing make up fun? **N** **Y**

Being popular is important - yes? **Y**

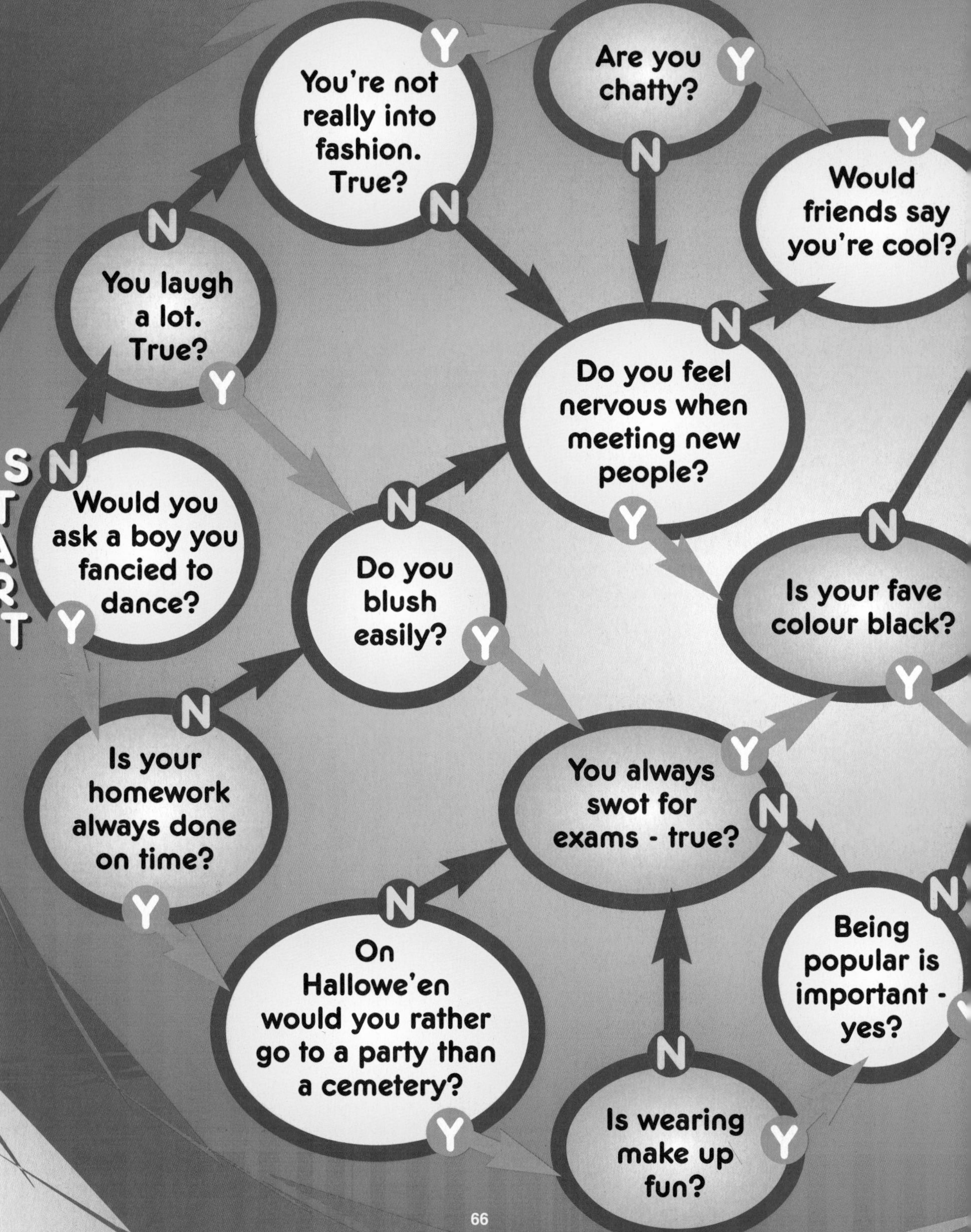

# y PaL?

Do you feel faint at the sight of blood?

**N**

**Y**

**Y**

Are you good at most school subjects?

**N**

Are you sometimes in trouble at school?

**N**

You sometimes disobey Mum - true?

**Y**

**N**

Do you love to dance?

**Y**

**N**

Do you enjoy scaring your friends?

**Y**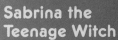

### Wednesday Addams

Wednesday would be your ideal spooky pal. You're both serious, intelligent and have a dark side to your nature. Like Wednesday, however, you can be a little shy around strangers which makes you feel awkward at times. Why not try to be a bit more outgoing and make some new friends?

### Buffy the Vampire Slayer

You and Buffy are clever, fit and super-cool! You enjoy looking good but can both be very serious and, sometimes, this can get in the way of having fun! Take more time to try different things and you could find that life becomes a lot more interesting for you and your mates.

### Sabrina the Teenage Witch

You're friendly, funny and very popular, so you and Sabrina would make brill mates. But, also like Sabrina, you can sometimes make mistakes and feel insecure. You could find that trying out new things, which can be a little scary, would help to build up your confidence.

# Mandy's Mega

**N** Nails! Turn to page 12 to find out how to have the nicest nails never. Ooops, we mean ever, of course! Also necks 'n' noses – but not knees!

**O** Orlando! Yep. Orlando in Florida, or Orlando Bloom. We don't really mind which cos we love 'em both. O is also for orange – one of our fave colours and fruits.

**Q** What are our favourite Q words? Questions and quizzes, that's what. And there are loads 'n' loads of quizzes in this book. So get quizzing – quickly!

**R** Reading! We know you all love reading, because you wouldn't be looking at this book if you didn't! But we also love rabbits, rugby, recycling and rounders.

Orlando in Orlando? Maybe not, but we love him anywhere!

P–pick up a penguin – either kind!

**P** Pals! Pocket money! Pizza! Penguins! We've got lots and lots of P words. But our favourite of all is presents! Christmas pressies, birthday pressies or just everyday pressies. They're perfect.

# A to Z

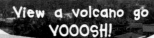
View a volcano go VOOOSH!

**S** School! Maybe we don't love it all the time, but school is pretty important to us. After all, that's where me meet loads of mate. Other fave S word are shopping, stars and surprises! Super!

**T** Texts – or should that be txts? We ol luv sndng thm, dnt we? Also teddy bears, toffee, toast, tasty treats and TV.

Teddy bears 'n' toffee. A tasty treat for a toy!

**U** Umbrella! You just can't beat a good old brolly. It's the No 1 British fashion accessory. (See W for more information.)

Umbrellas at Wimbledon. A regular summer sight.

**V** Vacation! The American word for holiday – but we like it. And while on vacation, we might just visit a volcano, or view the vista in a valley!

**W** Weather! The No 1 topic of conversation in Britain. Whether it's warm or windy, we'll waffle on about it for hours. And don't forget your wellingtons on a wet winter weekend. Or your umbrella at Wimbledon. (See U.)

**X** Xmas! The shortened form of Christmas makes us think of parties, pressies and kisses under the mistletoe. x x x x x

Yoghurt may not make you yodel – but it is yummy!

**Y** Yoghurt! Yum! Yum! It's our favourite snack. Other Y words we like include yachts, yes, yodel and yawn, which leads us to....

**Z** ZZZZZZZZZZZ! Time for bed and a nice long sleep. Goodnight!

# Boredom

We all have times when we feel as if we've nothing to do - and we're BORED! Worry no more, cos here are two pages packed with ideas to brighten your dullest days!

## COOK UP A STORM

Well, maybe not a storm, but loads of lovely goodies to nosh. Try out something special - or perfect an old favourite. Mmmm! Always ask permission, of course.

## LOOKIN' GOOD

Get together with a friend and give yourselves facials. Cucumber slices on your eyes are very relaxing and good for your skin. And face masks leave you feeling great, too. Remember to lock the door, though, as there's no way you want big brother walking in on you while you're looking like creatures from a horror movie.

## SPOOKED!

All you need to create some great spooky sounds is a tape recorder and a good imagination. Try taping the sound made when you pull your finger along the top of a comb, or a squeaky door, or paper rustling, or anything else you can think of. Then, when you've finished, invite some friends round, put out the light turn on your tape - and prepa to be spooked!

## DRESS TO IMPRESS

Turn the clock back to when you were a toddler, and dress up. Raid Mum's, or better still Gran's, wardrobe or old clothes store and put together the weirdest outfits you can create. Honestly, it'll be a hoot. Just remember not to answer the door bell if it rings.

## TIME TO TALK

Get a budgie (or two) and teach it to talk. Hours of amusement for everyone here.

70

# Beaters!

## WINDOW SHOPPING

Just because you've no money, doesn't mean you can't go round the shops. In fact, when you're broke is a good time to gather a group of mates and do some serious window shopping. Try making a list of all the expensive make up you would buy if you had loadsa money, or see who can find the best bargain. Honestly, if you like shopping, you'll find this lots of fun.

## PET PATROL

Take the dog for a walk - and if you don't own a dog, borrow a neighbour's or a friend's. Not only is it good exercise, but you never know *who* you might meet while you're out walking.

## PLAY TIME

Get together with some friends and put on your own play or pantomime. You'll have hours of fun planning and even more fun performing.

## PHONE A FRIEND

It sounds obvious, but chatting to a friend will make you feel much better. Always ask permission before using the phone, though - unless you pay your own bills of course.

## HELPING HAND

Fill your days by helping others. Find out if there is anyone near you who needs help with shopping - or just needs someone to chat to.

## FIT FOR FUN

With a mate, choose your favourite music and work out a dance or exercise routine. It'll be fun - and good for you, too.

## HUNT AND SEEK

Ask an adult to make a list of things in your area and then, on your own or with a few mates, set about trying to find them all. Things to 'hunt' can be actual places like a church with a spire, or more obscure things such as a house with three vowels in its name. Happy hunting.

# starscope

## Let's look at Leo, Virgo, Libra and Scorpio

## LEO   July 24 - Aug 23

You're outgoing, cheerful and bright, which isn't really all that surprising when you realise that your sign is ruled by the sun. You like to stand out in any crowd and are likely to have lots of hobbies and interests. You're also a fire sign, so you do have to be careful to control your temper at times - especially with younger people. Someone new could come on the scene this autumn, bringing big changes to some parts of your life. But don't worry, cos it'll all be great fun!

*Lucky month:* February
*Lucky colour:* Yellow
*Lucky number:* 3
*Lucky charm:* Pebble

## VIRGO   Aug 24 - Sept 23

Like Gemini, your sign is ruled by Mercury, so you love learning new things. However, you can be quite shy - especially when you meet people for the first time - and as a result, some people may think you're slightly snobbish. You like things to be neat and tidy and, while you enjoy going around in a crowd, there are times you prefer to be on your own with a good book. A special or surprise holiday could bring some unexpected fun for you this summer. Enjoy!

*Lucky month:* March
*Lucky colour:* Cream
*Lucky number:* 4
*Lucky flower:* Tulip

## LIBRA   Sept 24 - Oct 23

This is the sign of the scales - and that suits your well-balanced personality exactly. You make a loyal and trustworthy friend who can always be relied upon in an emergency, yet your love of dancing and having fun means that you're also a bit of a party princess. Your ruling planet is Venus, so you are likely to have loads more friends than enemies. Someone you know could share a surprising secret with you in June or July. Don't pass on the news - no matter how much you want to.

*Lucky month:* December
*Lucky colour:* Green
*Lucky number:* 9
*Lucky word:* Float

## SCORPIO   Oct 24 - Nov 22

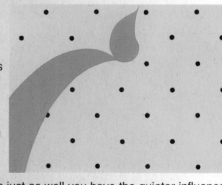

Lucky old you, cos you're ruled by two planets - Mars and Pluto. However, as Mars means you have a tendency to be hot-headed, it's just as well you have the quieter influence of Pluto to help you keep your temper in check. Friends mean a lot to you and you are likely to have mates of all ages. You also have a cool sense of humour and love playing jokes on people. There could be a big family surprise coming your way in December, so prepare for fun, fun, fun!

*Lucky month:* October
*Lucky colour:* Red
*Lucky number:* 11
*Lucky letter:* V

MORE ON PAGE 118

# SOUNDS RIGHT!

Lizzie was usually very organised when it came to Christmas presents. But this year she had a problem —

I just can't think *what* to buy Mum.

I'd love to record this song I've written for her, but I've no idea how to go about recording. Oh, well, I suppose I'll end up buying perfume, as usual.

Then a few days later, as Lizzie walked to school with her friend, Carly —

Really?

There's that new girl up ahead. Alison says her mum is a singer and has her own recording studio at home.

So they say — but I don't believe a word of it. Sophie's too boring to have an interesting mum.

Maybe so. But it might be neat to find out the truth.

So —

Hi, Sophie. You look fed up. You can chum up with me, if you like. I know it's no fun being new.

Thanks, Lizzie. I have been feeling a bit out of things.

74

But maybe not. I feel guilty about why I made friends with Sophie, cos now I really like her as a mate.

*But later —*

Hi, Lizzie. I've been telling my mum about your songs, and she'd like to hear them. Would you like to pop round tomorrow afternoon?

Sure. But I thought she was working.

Only in the morning. She's free any time after lunch.

Cool! I'll come round then.

*So —*

Hi, Lizzie. I'm really looking forward to this. If you're interested, we could record some of the songs later.

Really? But how? I — I thought you were a fitness instructor.

I am — but I'm a singer, too, and I have a small recording studio in the house. Come on. Let's see what we can do.

THE END

# RED

## More cring

During the school holidays I was in a large store when I spotted a boy I was trying to avoid. Quickly I turned away – and walked straight into a man who was standing nearby. The man dropped his parcel and I screamed in fright, so everybod – including the boy – noticed me.
*Chloe, Manchester.*

One day, while as was at my friend's house, I was clowning around and pretending to be a pop star. I was dancing wildly and singing 'into' a hairbrush microphone, when I suddenly realised that her mum and dad were at the door, watching me. It was sooo embarrassing! I wasn't half glad that I was going away on holiday the next day.
*Suzie, Workington.*

# FACED!

...orthy catastrophes.

...n class one day, my English teacher asked
...me a question. I wasn't really paying much
...attention and, instead of saying, "Yes, Miss",
I said, "Yes, Mum"! How embarrassing was that?
*Fiona, Dundee.*

When I was in Minorca
the hotel organised a 'pop idol'
competition. Some of the people
I'd met were entering and they talked
...e into taking part, too. I was so nervous
...forgot the words of the song I was singing.
I just sang "la, la, la" for almost
the entire second verse. People
said it still sounded good, but
I was really embarrassed.
Needless to say
I didn't win!
*Katie, London.*

While in town one Saturday I
was going up an escalator when
I noticed some boys from my
school. I was so busy watching
them that I didn't realise I had
reached the top and I fell
over in a heap. Of course,
everyone turned to look and
my face turned a brilliant red.
*Jill, Stratford.*

My most embarrassing moment was when I fell
off my seat in History class. As I fell, I
grabbed my friend to steady myself – and
she and her desk crashed to
the floor, too. Ooops!
*Nicole, Dublin.*

# ALL About

## Try this cool quiz to find out what makes you tick.

### Pick your favourite fruit!

**a.**

**b.**

**c.**

### Which pic catches your eye?

**a.**

**b.**

**c.**

### Who's your number 1 pin up?

**a.**

**b.**

**c.**

# YOU!

## Which is cutest?

a.

b.

c.

## What type of holiday do you fancy?

a.

**TRANSUN**
**Lapland**
The magical home of the real Father Christmas
b.

**Paris**
Travel Service
Bringing You The Best Of The Magic
**DISNEYLAND** RESORT
PARIS
FREE NIGHTS
KIDS FREE
c.

## Which pose do you like best?

a.

b.

c.

## Choose a book

**ANIMAL ARK**
Where animals come first
**Koalas in a Crisis**
LUCY DANIELS
a.

**PARTY GIRLS**
Lauren's Spooky Sleepover
Jennie Walters
c.

The **Ivy Crown**
Gill Vickery
WINNER OF THE FIDLER FIRST NOVEL AWARD
b.

81

**a.**

## Choose your favourite clothes.

**b.**

**c.**

**a.**

## Pick your favourite fashion shot

**c.**

**b.**

## Which of these coloured shapes do you like best?

**a.**

**c.**

**b.**

# Now add up your score

## Mostly a

Miss Average, that's you. You tend to be a bit on the quiet side - but that doesn't mean you're boring! Oh, no! You're likely to be friendly with most people in your class - boys as well as girls - and even the teachers don't mind having you around. However, you don't *always* have to agree with what everyone else says or thinks, you know. Try speaking up for yourself and putting your own ideas across from time to time. You might actually find it fun to be the leader of the gang now and again!

## Mostly b

You're little Miss Original so, when it comes to being different, you know all the tricks. If there's a choice to be made, then you can always be relied on to choose the most unusual option and you're certainly not slow to take the lead. While your wacky nature makes you popular with your mates - and you've probably got lots - some people may find you a bit overpowering at times. Remember, everyone is entitled to an opinion, and just because someone disagrees with you, it doesn't mean they are wrong!

## Mostly c

Stand up and take a bow, Miss Popular! You're confident, cheerful and fun to be around. You have lots of original thoughts and ideas, but you don't mind listening to what other people have to say, too. You're probably in great demand as a friend - but before you get too carried away, be warned that some people could mistake your confidence for smugness and, as a result, see you as a threat or a rival. You also need to remember that life's not *all* about fun! You have to spend time on work, too, you know.

# Wee Slavey

Your sandwiches, Ma'am.

NELLIE Perks was a young maidservant in the Victorian household of Sir William Selby-Smythe and his family. One day, Lady Selby-Smythe and her daughters, Flora and Alice, were entertaining a snobbish acquaintance —

Thank you, Nellie. Put them over there.

*Aah!*

Clumsy girl!

Sorry, Ma'am. I didn't see that hat box.

Tch! Mrs Cofton should have put it back on the table, where I left it!

A dustpan and brush? How quaint! At Cofton Hall we have purchased a most efficient *mechanical* carpet cleaner. The 'Little Wizard'. But, of course, Hugo's business is thriving so *I* can afford to spend freely.

What a mess you have made, Nellie! Clear it up immediately.

Yes, Ma'am.

*Ooh!* How dare that woman insinuate that we are hard up? I intend to show her that we can spend freely, too!

Wonderful! Are you going to buy us all new hats, Mother?

No, Alice. I intend to purchase a 'Little Wizard' cleaner! Make an appointment for a salesman to call, Nellie.

Yes, Ma'am. Shall I arrange it for after Sir William has returned from his business trip?

Certainly not! I want the man to come immediately!

So, next day —

Good morning, Lady Selby-Smythe. I am proud to introduce the 'Little Wizard' cleaner — a machine which will change the lives of both you and your servants.

The staff is assembled to watch your demonstration, Mr Beeks.

. . . see the evidence with your own eyes.

Lawks! That's *soot* he's pouring on the carpet!

Then we will begin. This little beauty is as good as two maids. The powerful suction cleans your carpet in half the time. But don't take my word for it . . .

And *flour!*

My carpet! I feel faint!

Do not fret, Madam. Watch!

There! Every grain is swept away.

It's like magic!

Indeed it is, Miss. And the machine is simplicity itself to use. Why, even this slip of a girl could operate it!

Come on, Nellie. Try it out!

Just turn the handle. The 'Little Wizard' does the rest.

Little? Huh! It looks big to me — and it's heavy, too.

You see! This machine will change your life, Madam.

*We* shall be able to show off to our friends now, like Mrs Cofton did to us!

Come into the study, Mr Beeks, and I will arrange payment.

*After Mr Beeks had left —*

I would like you to clean upstairs, Nellie.

With that thing?

Of course! You have had training with it, so naturally you should be the person who operates it.

Do try and look more cheerful, Nellie. You are very fortunate to be able to use such a labour-saving device.

Indeed. Other people would doubtless *love* to be employed by such a go-ahead household. Why, I almost envy you!

Huh! It's all right for Miss Flora and Miss Alice. They don't have to work the wretched thing!

According to the salesman, it will take you half the time to clean from now on. But don't worry, Nellie, I shall find other tasks to fill your day.

Except mine! Phew! This thing's very heavy to move around.

Nellie could learn to dress our hair!

And manicure our nails! The salesman was right. The 'Little Wizard' is going to improve *all* our lives!

86

And —

I'm worn out. It was all right for that strong salesman, but I can't generate the same amount of suction, no matter *how* fast I turn the handle!

Little Wizard

By the end of the day —

You look done in, Nellie. Have a cup of tea.

Thanks, Cook. That 'Little Wizard's' finished me!

Oh, no! They want me upstairs!

You'd better answer the bell. It's more than your job's worth to ignore it.

So —

Why isn't this table polished, Nellie? I distinctly told you to do it today.

I'm sorry, Ma'am. It took me all my time to clean the carpets with that new-fangled machine.

But the 'Little Wizard' *saves* time, Nellie. If you can't use modern, labour-saving devices, I shall have to look for a maid who can.

Lawks! They're expecting me to manage more work, when I'll actually have less time!

*Next day —*

Good to have you home, Master Algy. And how was school?

Boring — as usual, Roach.

I like Master Algy, but now he's home, it means *another* room to keep clean and tidy.

*But —*

This machine is brilliant fun, Nellie! I've cleaned Mama's bedroom carpet in no time!

Good! Perhaps he'll do the other bedrooms, too.

*However —*

Huh! Master Algy's tired of the 'Little Wizard' already. Looks like it's up to me again.

Do get a move on, Nellie. We've a busy day. Sir William is arriving home, and we're hosting a reception this evening.

*Then —*

Nellie! Nellie!

Now what?

My diamond clasp has gone missing! I took it out this morning, and now it's gone. Search the house from top to bottom!

Yes, Ma'am.

*But —*

There's no sign of the clasp anywhere, Ma'am.

What's going on?

William! How glad I am to see you. We have a crisis!

88

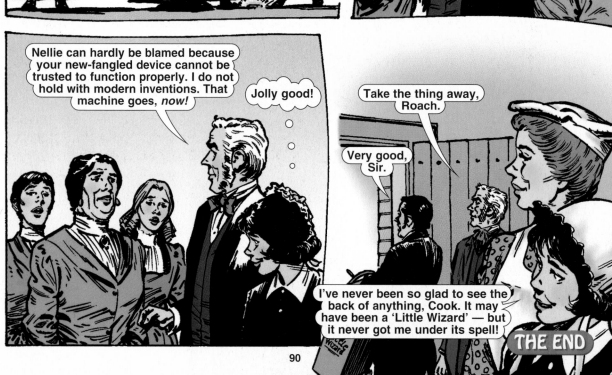

90

# SO YOU WANT TO BE A MODEL?

It'll be fab! You'll appear in all the best mags, wearing the best clothes, the latest make up and hairstyles? Right? Wrong!

**Modelling can be fun, but there are boring bits, too.**

No model appears in front of the camera looking fab without help. On each shoot there will be a make up artist, hair stylist, fashion editor and photographer, all working hard to make you look your best. And, while they work, you've to sit still, saying nothing.

If there are other models there, you may get a chance to chat between shots. But often, while **you're** having **your** look created, the other models will be being photographed and vice versa. So you could find yourself doing nothing but waiting for long periods of time. All the supermodels know this and take books, magazines and even knitting to pass the time!

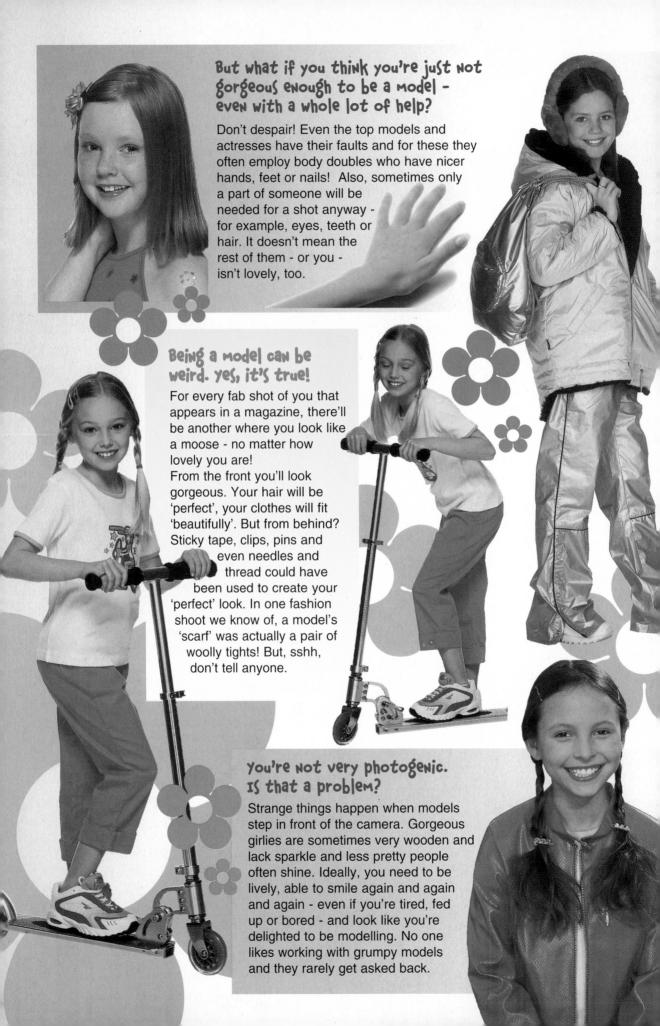

## But what if you think you're just not gorgeous enough to be a model - even with a whole lot of help?

Don't despair! Even the top models and actresses have their faults and for these they often employ body doubles who have nicer hands, feet or nails! Also, sometimes only a part of someone will be needed for a shot anyway - for example, eyes, teeth or hair. It doesn't mean the rest of them - or you - isn't lovely, too.

## Being a model can be weird. Yes, it's true!

For every fab shot of you that appears in a magazine, there'll be another where you look like a moose - no matter how lovely you are!
From the front you'll look gorgeous. Your hair will be 'perfect', your clothes will fit 'beautifully'. But from behind? Sticky tape, clips, pins and even needles and thread could have been used to create your 'perfect' look. In one fashion shoot we know of, a model's 'scarf' was actually a pair of woolly tights! But, sshh, don't tell anyone.

## You're not very photogenic. Is that a problem?

Strange things happen when models step in front of the camera. Gorgeous girlies are sometimes very wooden and lack sparkle and less pretty people often shine. Ideally, you need to be lively, able to smile again and again and again - even if you're tired, fed up or bored - and look like you're delighted to be modelling. No one likes working with grumpy models and they rarely get asked back.

## hat if you don't ke the things you've wear?

a word - tough! Models rely get to choose what they ear, but then modelling what u're given is what you get id for! It's unlikely that a list will choose anything at's too horrible for you to ear, though!

d, unfortunately, you'll rdly ever get to keep what u've modelled. The stylist ll be able to tell you where get it, however.

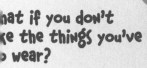

## I've been chosen for a shoot. what do I do?

Ask what they want. Models should turn up with freshly washed hair and wearing no make up or nail varnish. This leaves a 'blank canvas' for the professionals to work on. You may be asked to bring your fave clothes or a selection of accessories but, usually, everything is provided. Make sure you know in advance where you're going and ensure you arrive on time. The make up artist, hair stylist and photographer will all be waiting for you - and they are often paid by the hour. Do what you're asked, enjoy yourself, then wait to see yourself in print!

### The boring bit

If you've read all this and still want to be a model, apply to join a model agency. You'll find addresses for local agencies in your telephone directory. If they accept you, they'll feature your photograph and details in their latest catalogue. You shouldn't be asked to pay to have these photographs taken. Then, if someone wants you for a shoot, they'll contact the agency and the agency will contact you - it's as simple as that!

Good luck!

# FOLLOW ME!

**Sherry had been looking forward to her holiday for months — but now it seemed that nothing was working out the way she had hoped, thanks to the stupid legend.**

SHERRY and her family had only just arrived at the hotel when one of the guests told them about the woman in black — a ghostly spirit who, according to the locals, lured young people on to the dangerous quicksands on the north beach. It all seemed really unlikely to Sherry, because the north beach was surrounded by high mesh fencing, but it seemed that people had found their way past, and then totally disappeared. What was worse for Sherry, was that Mum seemed to believe the story, and had banned Sherry from going near *any* of the beaches on her own.

Upstairs, as Sherry stood on her balcony, she caught sight of her brother standing below. She loved Steve dearly, but he never seemed to want her around. As she wiped away the tears that threatened to fall, she realised that Steve was staring at something in the distance.

SHERRY followed his gaze and shuddered. In the shadow of some trees stood a strange, dark-haired woman wearing a long-sleeved black gown. But it was her face that made Sherry shudder, with its pale, hollow cheeks and shadowed eyes. Sherry gasped, breathless with horror. It was her! The woman in black!

Suddenly Sherry heard Dad calling to Steve and, as the boy turned, the woman disappeared. It was the scariest thing Sherry had ever seen. And what did it mean? Now that the woman had seen Steve, would she come back for him?

That evening, Sherry noticed that Steve was in a strange mood. Sherry guessed he was worrying about the woman and, after dinner, she followed him outside.

"What's wrong, Steve?" she asked. "Are you worried about the woman who was watching you this morning."

Steve stiffened. "I never saw any woman."

"Don't lie!" Sherry said crossly. "I watched you

stare at each other for at least five minutes!"

"Shut up, Sherry!" Steve shouted as he moved away, his face angry with fear. "Stop acting like a stupid baby and leave me alone!"

Sherry gazed after him, hurt and confused. Why wouldn't Steve admit he'd seen the woman? Was he really so afraid? He needed protecting, Sherry decided, and from now on she'd follow him secretly to keep him safe.

STRAIGHT after breakfast Steve went outside and, while Sherry hid nearby, the woman appeared and beckoned Steve to follow her.

Sherry followed them at a distance, but she soon realised that her brother wasn't even aware of her. It was as if he was sleepwalking. Every so often the woman turned to make sure Steve was still following and she smiled — an evil horrible smile that made Sherry's skin crawl. Over the road they went, then across the sand dunes and on towards the beach — the dangerous north beach, just as Sherry expected.

PANIC bubbled in her throat as Sherry saw her brother clamber through a hole in the fencing. She called out to him to stop – but Steve didn't seem to hear. He carried on, as if in a dream.

Quickly, Sherry scrambled through the fencing on to the beach. Then, all of a sudden it was as if the ground gave way beneath her, and her feet and legs were sucked down into the soft, wet quicksand.

"Help! Help me!" she screamed, spreading her arms to stop herself sinking.

She looked wildly about her, but the beach was deserted — except for the woman and Steve.

"Steve . . ." she begged. "It's me. Sherry! You-you've got to help me!"

Suddenly, Steve swivelled round, a dazed look on his face. When he saw Sherry struggling in the quicksand, he snapped awake, eyes widening with horror.

"Sherry!" he called, stumbling towards her as he unbuckled his belt. Then he stretched full length on the sand and threw one end of the belt to his sister. "Grab this, Sherry — I'll pull you out."

Sherry snatched at the belt. Like invisible hands, the quicksand tugged at her legs, trying to hold her tight. But Steve was strong, and Sherry felt herself being pulled free. She rose and rose until she was once again on safe, solid ground.

"Oh, Steve!" Sherry gasped, wiping grit from her cheeks. "You did it — you saved me!"

SUDDENLY, they heard a furious howl and, as they turned, something strange and wonderful started to happen — the woman in black began to fade. First her feet disappeared, then her body and shoulders and finally her evil, haunted face. Within seconds, the dreadful creature had gone. And deep inside, Sherry knew she'd never return.

"You did it, Steve — you destroyed her. When you escaped from her to save me, you somehow broke the spell."

Steve nodded, solemnly hugging his sister and staring at the empty beach. The woman in black was gone. Thanks to them, she would never lure anyone else on to the dangerous quicksands of the north beach.

—THE END—

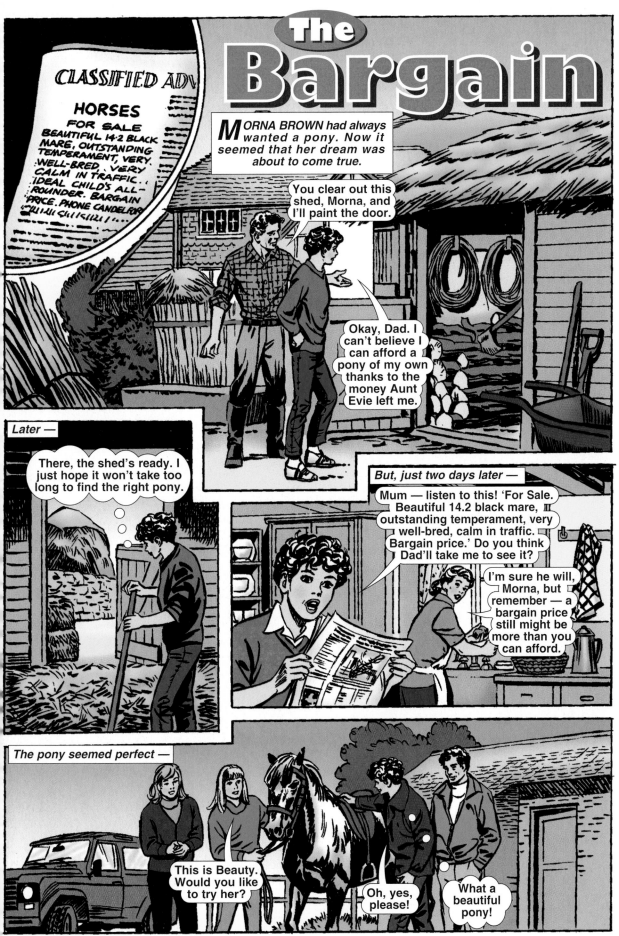

# The Bargain

MORNA BROWN had always wanted a pony. Now it seemed that her dream was about to come true.

You clear out this shed, Morna, and I'll paint the door.

Okay, Dad. I can't believe I can afford a pony of my own thanks to the money Aunt Evie left me.

CLASSIFIED ADV

HORSES
FOR SALE
BEAUTIFUL 14.2 BLACK MARE, OUTSTANDING TEMPERAMENT, VERY WELL-BRED, VERY CALM IN TRAFFIC. IDEAL CHILD'S ALL-ROUNDER. BARGAIN PRICE. PHONE CANDELFOR...

Later —

There, the shed's ready. I just hope it won't take too long to find the right pony.

But, just two days later —

Mum — listen to this! 'For Sale. Beautiful 14.2 black mare, outstanding temperament, very well-bred, calm in traffic. Bargain price.' Do you think Dad'll take me to see it?

I'm sure he will, Morna, but remember — a bargain price still might be more than you can afford.

The pony seemed perfect —

This is Beauty. Would you like to try her?

Oh, yes, please!

What a beautiful pony!

You're gorgeous, Beauty! Let's see if you can jump. I learned to jump a bit at riding school.

*To Morna's delight —*

Wow! You *can* jump!

Better than *I* can. But surely she'll cost too much?

*However —*

Yes, it really is a bargain price. We didn't pay a lot for Beauty and Laura's just too busy with schoolwork now to ride her.

Then I'm sure Morna would like her — once my vet checks her over.

*A few days later —*

Well — good luck with Beauty, Morna.

Thank you, Laura.

Laura hasn't patted Beauty goodbye and she doesn't seem upset. Perhaps she just isn't very keen on ponies.

Here are all Beauty's papers, Morna. Her vaccination certificate, details of her breeding and the receipt from her last owner.

Thanks!

*Soon —*

Here's your new home, Beauty. I'm sure we're going to have a wonderful time together.

Don't you want to explore your stable, Beauty?

Most ponies examine everything new, but Beauty doesn't seem interested.

I-I'll be back later, Beauty.

How odd! I feel as if she's waiting for me to go.

*Later, Morna read Beauty's papers —*

Beauty's ancestors go right back to Victorian times. There have been several black mares called Beauty — and there are newspaper cuttings, too.

Wow! This horse in 1892 looks identical to Beauty. Her family must have bred true to type, all through the generations.

BEAUTY, MISS AMELIA DE VERE'S MARE, AT THE NATIONAL SHOW 1892

Supper's ready, Morna.

Coming, Mum.

There are a few more bits and pieces, but I'll read them another time.

*After supper —*

I'm glad you've eaten your hay, Beauty. I've brought a carrot for you, too.

What a cold draught. And I almost felt as though there was something behind me. Beauty isn't scared, though.

I'll be glad to get indoors. Tomorrow, I'll take Beauty for a ride.

*Next day —*

This is wonderful, Beauty. When we get up on to the open downs, we can have a gallop.

You're really fast, Beauty, but I know I can stop you.

Good girl.

She's lovely! She really *was* a bargain at the price I paid for her!

*Then —*

Urgh, what a horrible change in the weather. I can hardly see the path, but *you* can, can't you, Beauty?

101

Oh, Beauty, you *are* lovely, but there's something *strange* about you. You seem sad and distant.

*That night —*

What was that? It sounded like hooves in the yard.

Someone's riding Beauty — side-saddle — and in strange clothes! I'll wake Dad!

*But, in Beauty's stable —*

You must have been dreaming, Morna. Beauty's right here.

But, Dad, look! Beauty's sweating as if she's been ridden.

*Next morning —*

I'll check Beauty's records to see if any previous owners noticed anything unusual about her.

# PICK A PUZZLE!

## Two pages packed with puzzles for you!

## CRaZy CoNTenTS!

**Unravel the letters to find out what's inside each container.**

## ALL CHANGE!

Replace the first letter of each colour pair with a new letter to make different words. The new first letter will be different for each pair. (e.g : YELLOW and PINK become MELLOW and MINK)

**BLUE** | **RED** | **PINK**
**ORANGE** | **YELLOW** | **BLACK**

## COOL COLOURS!

Cross out the letters which appear three or more times in each square and you'll reveal cool eyeshadow colours!

```
G R B N O
O K A G S
N R L K A
S A U O R
G K E N S
```

```
O S Y P N
A K U A S
K O N Y R
P Y S O K
N L A E S
```

```
B M U O L
F P R B F
R U I L M
L O M N U
R B F O K
```

## FAST FLOW

Quickly - draw a line to the correct colour for each flower

buttercup
daisy
lilac
daffodil
lily
sunflower
snowdrop
forget-me-not
primrose
violet

**WHITE**

**YELLOW**

**BLUE**

| B | G | N | I | R | A | G | I | H | R |
|---|---|---|---|---|---|---|---|---|---|
| B | A | N | J | T | H | S | T | A | H |
| F | I | D | R | A | C | T | E | T | L |
| M | C | I | G | A | O | I | K | E | Q |
| T | K | S | R | E | A | E | Y | K | G |
| S | D | E | F | M | T | E | P | C | N |
| H | S | O | C | K | S | O | U | A | O |
| I | S | H | I | R | T | O | P | J | R |
| R | N | S | E | S | T | O | O | B | A |
| T | R | J | S | T | I | G | H | T | S |

# SHORTS!

Find the following short words, all of which you can wear, hidden up, down, backwards, forwards or diagonally in our wordsearch.

badge, boots, cardi, coat, hat,

jacket, jersey, mini, ring,

scarf, shirt, shoes, skirt,

socks, sarong, tights, t-shirt, top.

# words! words! words!

How many words of more than three letters can you make using the letters in this word?
## MULTICOLOURED!

### Scores
20–30    cool yellow!
31–40    warm orange!
40 +     red hot!

# LOOKING

## Sukie and Tilda were very fashion conscious —

What do you think, Tilda? Should I wear the pink or purple top with this skirt?

Purple, I think.

I don't know. I like the pink one, too.

Don't worry, Sukie. You'll look great whatever you choose — *we* always look cool!

A few days later —

Hi, I'm Donna Allen. Can you tell me where the office is, please? It's my first day here.

We're Sukie and Tilda. The office is just inside the main door.

She seems nice, but her hair's a bit of a mess.

Yeah! And I wouldn't be seen dead with that schoolbag!

You know, what she needs is a makeover.

Yeah! We could make her look great!

# GOOD!

*So, next day —*

Have you ever thought of wearing your hair up, Donna? It would really suit you.

You think so? I might give it a go, then.

And if you made the knot in your tie smaller, you'd look more feminine.

You could look really fantastic if you put your mind to it, you know.

Yeah — with just a little make-up and some help with your clothes you'd look amazing.

Tell you what, come back to my place after school and we'll show you what we mean.

All right, but I'd better ring my sister, Chloe, to say I'll be late home.

*And, later, at Sukie's —*

I think this style would look good.

We could try a little make-up, too, if you'd like.

*A few days later —*

Are you coming to the disco on Friday, Donna?

Yes. I thought it would be a good way to meet everyone.

And show off your new look!

Cool!

What time should we come round on Thursday to do your makeover, Donna?

About sevenish? My sister's quite keen to watch. I hope you don't mind.

That's okay! We could give *her* some tips, too.

I don't know why you're letting *those* two give you a makeover. Their fashion sense is a joke!

Oh, I don't mind, Sarah. They're good fun and they mean well.

On Thursday —

Hello. You must be Donna's friends, Sukie and Tilda. I'm her sister, Chloe. Come in.

Oh! I don't believe it! It's Chloe Allen from Changing You — the fashion programme on TV!

It *is* Chloe Allen from Changing You, isn't it?

The one who does all the makeovers? Yeah! We can't tell her sister how to dress! What are we going to do?

But —

Donna says you'd all like some advice on what to wear to tomorrow's disco?

What? Oh, er, yes, we would.

Please!

Let's see what you've got then!

Erm, right.

THE END

# It's A Doodle

Almost everyone likes to doodle, but did you know that what you draw and the way you draw it can tell a lot about the type of person you are? Read on to find out more.

First thing to look at is what you actually draw. Some people draw recognisable shapes or figures, which show clearly what they are thinking about, while others  cover their books or papers with little squiggles and shapes. But just because the doodles are unrecognisable, it doesn't mean they don't tell a lot about your personality. Here are a few general rules to help you analyse the doodles of you and your friends.

 If the doodles go up the page, this shows someone who is cheerful and optimistic, while doodles going downwards show someone who is quieter and more of a pessimist. If you tend to draw straight across from one side to the other, it shows that you are level-headed and keep your cool in an emergency. If the doodles are very neat and regular, then you are probably an organised person, while someone who is always rushing about or is a dreamer, is more likely to draw lots of random doodles.

Size of doodles is also important. Are they large flourishes which sprawl everywhere? Many extrovert people do those sort of doodles, while shy, nervous people often draw tiny flowers or things hiding in corners.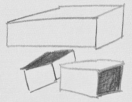

How heavy are the drawings? If there are heavy lines and lots and lots of colouring or shading, then this is the sort of person who takes life quite seriously and has very definite ideas  about things. If, however, the lines are very light and faint, this can either mean someone who is carefree and a bit thoughtless, or someone who is a little nervous and frightened of making too much fuss.

Definite shapes are easier to analyse as hearts usually mean the person is thinking about someone they like, while stars mean they want to be noticed. Someone who draws figures is probably thinking about what they want to do.

Next we'll look at the doodles of two readers. This will help you see how actual drawings are analysed.

## LYDIA

Lydia likes science and geography, and this is obvious when you look at her doodles. Can you see how her flower looks like a telescope? And look at the boat. It seems to have wheels. The little drawing at the bottom shows her love of travel, as you can see the elephant making his way across a river, toward a castle. Lydia doesn't press very hard on the page, which shows she

can be a little unsure of herself, but the detail on the castle shows that she thinks things through quite carefully. This is also shown by the fact that her doodles take up only around half the page. We can see that Lydia tends to be shy of people, because her doodles are mainly of objects - a flower, a bicycle and a landscape. **The only people in her doodles are two little pin figures, which are smaller than anything else.**

## SOPHIE

Sophie has a very different personality. She doesn't plan things out in such detail and tends to concentrate on one thing at a time. Notice that each of the doodles is just of one thing. The first one is a flower, the second is a series of squiggles, the third is a spiral and the fourth is a girl. She draws quite heavy lines, showing that she tries hard and takes life quite seriously. Unlike the spiky, scientific lines in Lydia's doodles, Sophie's rounded, circular doodles show someone who is emotional and more interested in people than objects. There are no bikes or castles in her drawings, and the largest picture is of a girl, which means Sophie has a very outgoing nature.

So now you know! No matter whether doodles are of stars, sailing ships or just simply squiggles, they all hold clues to your personality. Have fun!

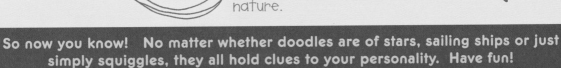

# COOL!

*BEST FRIENDS, Judy Jones and Mandy Taylor, lived next door to each other. One day during the Christmas holidays —*

I'm bored! I wish it would snow — then we could go sledging or skating.

Or throw snowballs and make a snowman!

*Next morning —*

Cool! It's snowed at last! I'll go round for Mandy after breakfast.

But —

I'm sorry, Judy — Mandy and Patch went to her aunt's in Milchester last night, and when it started snowing, Uncle Des insisted she stayed.

Aw!

I'll just have to play in the snow by myself.

Snowballs are no fun when you've no one to aim at. Maybe skating would be better . . .

The flooded meadow's frozen over! It's a safe place to skate.

Oops! I need a friend to hang on to. Skating's hopeless on your own!

But—

I know! I'll build a snowman! But I'll make it look like Mandy and add a snow dog like Patch. That should cheer me up!

This is no good! It looks nothing like Mandy or Patch.

Then —

I might as well give up.

Aargh!

Who threw that?

114

There's nobody there except my snow models and *they* can't throw snowballs!

Don't go, Judy!

Eh? That sounded like Mandy's voice!

It's as if my model's alive!

Of course it isn't! It's *me!*

Mandy!

The road from Milchester has been cleared, so I've come home! I wanted to play in the snow with you.

So —

Watch out! I've loadsa snowballs here!

Me, too, Mandy Taylor! And when we've thrown them all, we can go skating!

**THE END**

# it's christmas!

1. What did my true love give to me on the fifth day of Christmas?

2. Name the period of time leading up to Christmas.

3. In which pantomime does Buttons appear?

4. Can you come up with three Christmas names?

5. How many ugly sisters appear in Cinderella?

6. Which bird most often appears on Christmas cards?

7. Name the day after Christmas.

8. What name is given to a special Christmas song?

9. Who is the mean person who appears in 'A Christmas Carol'?

10. In what does Santa travel?

11. Under which plant do people kiss at Christmas?

12. What colour is Rudolph's nose?

13. What do we call it when it snows on Christmas Day?

14. Which green vegetables are traditionally eaten at Christmas?

**17.** What's another name for Christmas pudding?

**18.** Which winter plant has bright red berries?

**19.** A hat, motto, joke and gift can be found inside which noisy Christmas item?

**15.** Jack sells a cow for carrots in Jack and the Beanstalk. True or false?

**20.** There is a town called Santa Claus. True or false?

**16.** Which part of a turkey is pulled at Christmas?

**21.** Do mincemeat pies contain mince?

**22.** Who looked out 'on the feast of Stephen'?

**23.** What is traditionally hung up for Santa at Christmas?

**24.** 'We wish you a merry Christmas and a _ _ _ _ _ / _ _ _ / _ _ _ _!'

**25.** All snowflakes are different. True or false?

# answers

1. Five gold rings. 2. Advent. 3. Cinderella. 4. Carol, Holly, Noel...give yourself a gold star if you can come up with any more. 5. Two. 6. Robin. 7. Boxing Day. 8. Carol. 9. Ebenezer Scrooge. 10. Sleigh. 11. Mistletoe. 12. Red. 13. A white Christmas. 14. Brussels sprouts. 15. False. He sold the cow for beans. 16. Breastbone. 17. Plum or figgy pudding. 18. Holly. 19. Cracker. 20. True. It's in Indiana, USA. 21. No, it's a mixture of dried fruit and spices. 22. Good King Wenceslas. 23. A stocking. 24. Happy New Year. 25. True.

# starscope

### It's time for Sagittarius, Capricorn, Aquarius and Pisces.

## SAGITTARIUS Nov 23 - Dec 22

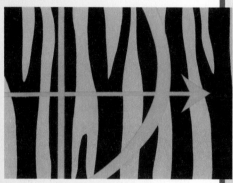

Girls born under this sign are outgoing, bright and good natured. Their ruling planet is Jupiter - the luckiest planet of all - and this means that Sagittarius girlies are usually successful at most things they try. Friends and friendship are very important to you, but friends shouldn't be too upset if you forget a birthday as forgetfulness (and carelessness) are two Sagittarius faults. Someone may have a surprise planned for you this year. Probably sometime over the summer. Oooo!

*Lucky month:* *July*
*Lucky colour:* *Blue*
*Lucky number:* *7*
*Lucky flower:* *Lily*

## CAPRICORN Dec 23 - Jan 21

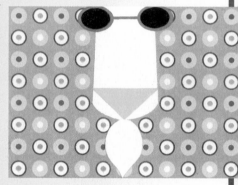

As a winter baby, you are sometimes seen to be cold and a bit distant. Nothing could be further from the truth, though, as your warm personality ensures that people who get to know you are usually friends for life. You're tidy and determined and, as you like things to be organised, you make a good leader. Your ruling planet is Saturn, which means you have to work hard for things you want. A message could be heading your way. Listen carefully, as it could be very important in the future.

*Lucky month:* *April*
*Lucky colour:* *Purple*
*Lucky number:* *21*
*Lucky letter:* *A*

## AQUARIUS Jan 22 - Feb 19

Aquarius girls are good listeners who always make themselves available if friends need to talk. Your ruling planets are Uranus and Saturn, so you are independent and clever. You do have a rebellious streak, though, and there is no way you can ever be made to do something if you don't want to. You could hear a bit of news sometime over the summer which will totally amaze you. Be sure to let everyone know, as this is something you won't want to keep to yourself.

*Lucky month:* *June*
*Lucky colour:* *Pink*
*Lucky number:* *6*
*Lucky charm:* *Leaf*

## PISCES Feb 20 - March 21

This is the dreamy, mysterious sign of the zodiac - probably due to the fact that Neptune is one of the ruling planets. Pisces girls are great at keeping secrets, so that makes them very popular as friends. However, on the down side, they are sometimes a bit lazy and hard to motivate. Pisces people are also good at solving problems - especially for other people. A visit or trip to a strange place, sometime in May or June, could be very exciting for all the family.

*Lucky month:* *November*
*Lucky colour:* *Lemon*
*Lucky number:* *18*
*Lucky word:* *Star*

# The Visitor

JANICE PALMER hadn't seen her aunt for ten years and was really looking forward to meeting up with her again. Aunt Sophie lived in Oregon, America —

This photo was taken the last time I saw Aunt Sophie. I bet we've both changed a lot since then.

It's years since we met, but she writes great letters and phones every couple of months. She can't wait to meet you, Tibs!

**But a few days before Aunt Sophie's visit —**

Reports are coming in of an explosion at the Long Springs Research Centre in Oregon, USA.

That's where Sophie works!

Oh, David, I hope she's not hurt!

**Dad tried to call Aunt Sophie, but —**

Why can't you speak to her, Dad?

Sophie's work is top secret, Jan. Security isn't allowing calls through.

**But a few hours later —**

Sophie! Oh, I'm so pleased to hear from you. We were really worried when we heard about the explosion.

119

And —

Sophie says it was just a small fire and that she's fine. She's still coming over.

Great!

*Two days later, on the way to the airport —*

It's almost twelve years since Sophie moved to America. In some ways it'll be like meeting someone new.

She'll notice how much weight you've put on!

Mum!

*The plane arrived on time —*

David!

Good to see you, sis.

How are you, Sophie?

Here you are, Jan — a present from America!

Thanks, Aunt Sophie. It's really cute!

*But, in the car —*

I don't want to be ungrateful, but it's *cat* things I collect! Aunt Sophie's never given me anything to do with *dogs* before!

Back home —

So this is the famous Tibs! No wonder you love him, Jan! He's cool.

A little later —

You really must come to America some time . . .

That's strange! Tibs is moving away. He only does that when he senses people don't like him. But Aunt Sophie is crazy about cats!

Aunt Sophie decided on an early night —

I think I'll turn in. I know there's lots to talk about, but I'm exhausted!

Jan will show you your room!

Sure!

I thought Aunt Sophie and I were going to be such good friends, but she's hardly spoken to me.

You've got the spare room at the end, Aunt Sophie. This is my room!

Looks like a really fine den, honey. Sleep tight!

A few minutes later —

'The first thing I must do when I arrive is see your room' — that's what Aunt Sophie said in her last letter. But she wasn't interested . . .

121

*Then —*

Go on, off you go!

Oops! Tibs must have settled down in the spare room. Looks like Aunt Sophie isn't crazy about *all* cats!

*Next day, the family visited a stately home —*

And if you look up, you can see a splendid example of stone carving . . .

I thought Aunt Sophie loved history, but she looks bored.

*Then —*

Sophie, what's happened to the birthmark on your shoulder?

What? Oh, *that!* I had it removed recently by laser. Didn't I mention it?

*On the way home —*

Aunt Sophie and I used to chat on the phone for ages, but she's hardly said a word to me today. She looks annoyed.

*Later —*

Oh, Aunt Sophie's on her mobile! I'd better not disturb her.

Why wasn't I told? That's *exactly* the sort of thing I should know!

I nearly ruined everything. It's not easy doing this.

Who's Aunt Sophie talking to? And what does she mean?

*Next morning, Janice took her aunt a cup of tea —*

Oh, Aunt Sophie's not here, but *Tibs* is! And he's making an awful mess!

*Janice tried to tidy up —*

Oh, no! A piece of paper's gone right under the bed!

What are you doing?

I — er — brought you some tea, b-but Tibs had knocked your bag over and . . .

I didn't mean to shout, Janice. I'm just still tired from my flight.

That's okay.

She really scared me then — and she's never called me *Janice* before! It's always been Jan.

*Aunt Sophie stayed in her room —*

Dad, do you think there's something a bit strange about Aunt Sophie? She seems different and...

Don't be silly, Jan. Aunt Sophie's just tired!

Actually, she's not as much fun as *I* remember, either, but her work is very stressful. She'll be fine when she's had a rest.

Maybe you're right, Dad.

But I'm gonna investigate this further.

*Next day, when Aunt Sophie was out—*

I'm sure that piece of paper had something important on it. I just hope it's still here.

Oh! What's this? It's like a fact file — all about *me!*

SUBJECT
*Janice Palmer*
PARENTS: David, Hilary
BORN: 20·3·92
HAIR: Brown
EYES: Brown
PETS: Cat, Tibs
HOBBIES: Swimming, reading, music, drawing,
AMBITION: To work with animals

Maybe *now* Mum and Dad will believe that something's up!

*And —*

Look, Dad! I found this in Aunt Sophie's room. It *proves* there's something going on.

You shouldn't have been snooping around, Jan.

But *why* would my sister need an information sheet about our Jan? And where is Sophie, anyway?

She went out, but she shouldn't be long.

124

Here she is now and . . . *oh!*

What is it, Jan?

*Two* Aunt Sophies!

No, I'm United States federal agent Lisa Melder, but *this* is your Aunt Sophie.

Hi, folks! Am I glad to see you!

*An explanation followed —*

After the explosion there was a chance some of us could have been contaminated by a chemical. We had to stay put until it could be proved that we were fine.

To let people think everything was okay, imposters — like me — took the place of people in the centre. Sophie gave me lots of information about you.

To make up for the deception, we'd like you to accept an all-expenses paid holiday to America.

Marvellous!

And I can stay an extra two weeks.

And the first thing I must do is see your room, Jan.

There's no doubt now that this *is* my real Aunt Sophie! This is going to be the best holiday ever!

125

**The End**